Catching Desire

Catching Desire

Carmelo Militano

Ekstasis Editions

Published in 2020 by:
Ekstasis Editions Canada Ltd.   Ekstasis Editions
Box 8474, Main Postal Outlet   Box 571
Victoria, B.C. V8W 3S1   Banff, Alberta T1L 1E3

LIBRARY AND ARCHIVES CANADA CATALOGUING IN PUBLICATION

Title: Catching desire / Carmelo Militano.
Names: Militano, Carmelo, author.
Identifiers: Canadiana (print) 20190205555 | Canadiana (ebook)
20190205563 | ISBN 9781771713481
   (softcover) | ISBN 9781771713498 (ebook)
Subjects: LCSH: Modigliani, Amedeo, 1884-1920—Poetry. | LCSH:
Modigliani, Amedeo, 1884-1920—Fiction.
Classification: LCC PS8626.I435 C38 2020 | DDC C811/.6—dc23

Canada Council   Conseil des Arts   Funded by the   Canadä
for the Arts   du Canada   Government
                                         of Canada

Ekstasis Editions acknowledges financial support for the publication of
Catching Desire from the government of Canada through the Canada Book
Fund and the Canada Council for the Arts, and from the Province of British
Columbia through the Book Publishing Tax Credit.

Printed and bound in Canada.

For my parents: Carmela Foti and Domenico Militano
And always: Vera, Adrianna, Tony, Rosa, and Pina

You must not grieve that the world is glimpsed
Through veils. How else should it be seen?
How will you strip away the veil of the eye, the veils
That you are, you who want to grasp the heart
Of things, who long to know their meanings

~ Sue Kwock Kim (*Monologue for an Onion*)

He who, no more than we, believed a public for art existed.
He who would be stupefied to know he has been betrayed by
absurd legends—having fabricated his own by hand—as one weaves
straw that can blaze up.

~ Jean Cocteau (*Modigliani*)

When I know your soul, I will paint your eyes.

~ Amedeo Modigliani

Part One: Family and Adolescence

A Son of the Stars

He declares early in his typhoid-induced fever that he wants to be an artist. His mother, Eugénia, however, notes he has not done so well on his exams of late and worries he is "chasing a shadow," this interest in art. She is uncertain whether to encourage or discourage his curiosity, his desire, his obvious ability.

Before Amedeo's birth, the family faced financial disaster. Eugénia's husband, Flamino, did not inherit the Modigliani family's financial skills, or luck. His banking shares and schemes collapsed. The mines in Sardinia, the lumber and charcoal trade started by Flamino's grandfather—an advisor to Napoleon, no less—failed. Eugénia concludes her husband has no business sense. Then new stresses and strains on the marriage. Silent distances emerge between them.

In her notebook Eugénia uses the metaphor that Dedo (the family nickname for Amedeo), at this point is like a "chrysalis," and it is impossible to predict what will emerge. Spiritually powerful, intellectually brilliant, charismatic and famous? Eugenia notes with pleasure her Amedeo is intelligent.

Eugénia is thoughtful, observant, protective, intellectual, pragmatic, and detached about the life gathering at her feet. Her family is both a harbour and oasis from the turbulence outside the home but by the time Amedeo reaches the age of three, Eugenia and Flamino no longer share the same bed yet they have produced three children.

She picks up Flamino's nightshirt from the bed in the back room of the apartment facing the garden (she thinks that he be the one to deal with the constant yapping of the dog next door in the neighbour's garden in the middle of the night) and looks it over at armslength. Her face is expressionless. She does not know him when darkness falls like a silent thud, when the candles are all snuffed. She shakes her head. She cannot not know him anymore. It is a mystery to outsiders what goes on in their marriage.

She knows she must be strong if she will save the family from Flamino's miscalculations, his carelessness, his repeated aloofness, his desperate silent pride.

It is not the first time she has been called upon to be resourceful and resolute, to save the family from the cruel verities of the street.

One time, Eugénia had piled everything in the apartment on top the bed where she lay pregnant with Amedeo, just before the bailiffs arrived to collect on the family debts. She directed Laure her sister, to stack the kitchen chairs in one corner of the bed in front of her, and in the other corner stack the family dishes and cutlery. They placed the table over her and on top of the table placed books and clothes. The bed sagged under the successive waves of belongings carefully heaped onto the bed; it eventually looked like a vast 19th century junk heap with a female head sticking out at one end, beaded with sweat. They both knew the law of the land prevented bailiffs from possessing anything on a bed from a pregnant woman.

Eugénia remembers hearing shouts from the street below drift up through the open window before falling asleep. Laure kept the flies off her sister's face as she slept.

Shortly after giving birth, Eugénia and Laure start a private language school to put food on the table. The Garsins—Eugénia's family name—are intellectually and culturally superior to the Modigliani family. Eugénia can speak three languages: Italian, French, Spanish, also some Arabic. The Garsins see money as a necessity, but it is not to be valued for its own sake. The life of the mind and spirit is superior. The private language school prospers. She no longer needs her husband.

Dedo is her star pupil. Amedeo learns to read and write French quickly, the language of art, of love and seduction.

Later, as a young man in Paris, he reads the poetry of Villon, Baudelaire, Lautréamont, Verlaine. Drunk, he can declaim, in Italian with a perfect Tuscan pitch, Dante's *Inferno* in the cafés of Montparnasse: La Rotonde, Le Chat Noir, Café Danzig. Beatrice Hastings, poet and Amedeo's lover at the time, thinks he makes up the verses.

She thinks it is impossible for him to recite so much poetry after so much wine and hashish. Plus, no one gathered around the café tables understands Italian or has read the classics.

The rumour is that Beatrice speaks French with her British tongue in Modigliani's cheek.

Garsin Blood

Isaac, Eugénia's father, suffered from a nervous breakdown
Felt the gardeners were persecuting him
Became an embittered, irascible old man
Could shout in Italian, French, Spanish, or Greek perfectly.

Aunt Laure lived in and out of institutions
Convinced men waited patiently to rape her.
She could tell by the way a man stopped to light a cigarette
Cupped a match in the shape of her vagina
It twitched when he struck the box.
Or she once saw a man step off a tram
He held a black umbrella on a sunny day, twitch.
But she especially feared poets
Overcome with passion at any moment
Would grab her weak wrists
Pull her into the dark corner surrounded by trees
At the edge of the park where she walked.

Aunt Gabriella did not have a persecution complex,
Instead she killed herself in Rome
Threw herself down a flight of stairs
After, her apartment started to fill with blood.

Uncle Umberto asserted progress was devaluing
All his achievements in engineering
Decided it was futile to go on
And locked himself up in his studio.

But it was a multilingual family
Everyone spoke two or three languages
Read Nietzsche, Emerson, and Moses Mendelssohn
Bergson's *Matter and Memory*
Brought home like a captured eagle.
Eugénia proud of her family neuroses
Proved their intellectual and spiritual gifts,
Connection to Spinoza.

2

Beatrice Hastings, amazed at Modigliani's psychic powers
Superstitious, he claimed kinship with Nostradamus.
He could feel foul weather approaching
Sarcastic, offensive, he raged at friends, foes, and lovers
Slashed canvases, self-destructive without touching a drop.
When rain finally came, he became soft and gentle
Touched her right cheek with three fingers, cooed and kissed her neck
Modigliani in Paris, all Garsin blood

The Adolescent Apprentice

Dedo has abandoned his studies completely and does nothing but paint. He paints all day and every day—with a fervor and constancy that enchants and stupefies me.... His teacher is very satisfied and I, I can scarcely understand, for it seems that for having studied only three or four years he certainly paints not badly and draws really splendidly."
~ Eugénia Modigliani, April 10, 1899, in a letter to her sister Laure.

Livorno Diary #1: Light and Memory

I left for Livorno via Florence after spending three days in pretty Cesena and the picturesque seaside resort, Cesenatico, as a guest poet from Canada at the International Poetry Festival and the Sister Arts. It was my first time abroad as a poet/writer, and left me amazed and flattered at my reception. I met some Italian poets who were both serious and fun, and some fine, quiet, Romanian poets who offered me a ride back to my hotel after one night of poetry, song, and dance. It should have been a fifteen- or twenty-minute ride, but the driver—a burly fellow in a white linen jacket, and apparently an expert on Heidegger and a poet—managed to get lost in spite of the GPS in the car. His driving companion in the front seat was a starchy, bland-looking blonde who had read a poem describing hers or someone's orgasm and something about a picnic and a room in a city.

None of the Romanian poets spoke English, and only one of them spoke Italian. After about forty minutes they started arguing among themselves about the right direction to take. Meanwhile, a thin, white fog began to roll, or sometimes twisting slowly upward like a cartoon ghost minus the dark holes for eyes, off the dark, flat rice fields and haunted, narrow road. The entire countryside was beginning to resemble the background to a vast Italian Gothic novel. It was midnight and we were lost, and I was trapped in a car with four Romanian poets.

Martin Amis, in *The Information*, wrote: "Poets don't drive. Never trust a poet who can drive. Never trust a poet at the wheel. If he can drive, distrust the poetry."

I used to think Amis was merely being droll.

Before going to Cesena, I had spent three days in Novara with my cousin Pina's family and my sister who happened to be in Italy celebrating and toasting, somewhat ruefully, her stumble into late middle age. Respectfully, let us just say she turned somewhere between 50 and 55 years old.

My sister and I wandered about the town on two successive nights. One evening stands out when we happened to be near the Novara Cathedral. The street was empty and the streetlights and the fading light combined to create a still, melancholy mood. The white moon had risen in the sky above the cathedral and was shaped like a wedge of lemon in a luminous-blue-cocktail evening sky.

The day before, a series of serendipitous encounters and moments in the Art Bar and at the hairdresser turned her angst about her age around, but it left my cousin puzzled.

"*Ma che cosa ha combinato tu e tuo fratello?*" (What were you and your brother up to?), she exclaimed to her, after I left for Livorno.

There is no plausible explanation for remembering evening light and the rapture of baroque architecture.

I changed trains in Florence before continuing to Livorno and my quixotic quest to pick up a scent or perhaps a look into Modigliani's past. I hoped to try to see, as Modigliani had seen and felt, the Tuscan light before Paris, find 38 Via Roma (the main residence of the family, now Casa Modigliani), hear the soft hiss and lap of the sea at night, and admire the sturdy palm trees lining Viale Italia, that wide boulevard that hugs the seashore and leads to the old harbour.

At the Florence rail station, I had enough time before catching the train to buy an espresso, use the restroom, and to give the place a once-over. Here, I was looking…for anything really—the shape of a shop window, a café name, a gesture, a woman's scarf, even the look of the entrance to the station—that would evoke, perhaps no more than for a moment, a faded sliver but glimmer of familiarity from my own past.

It had been close to thirty years since I was last in the Florence train station, and my memories were, at best, sepia-coloured and flat. I was once a young man, mad with longing and desire for a pretty French/German girl from Aix-en-Provence by way of Paris, Vienna, and Munich, in this city.

I stopped to look around, a boulder in the stream of people flowing around me, trying to appear nonchalant and to not draw attention, but alas, images from my youth refused to float up to the surface. I was reminded, ironically, of one of Freud's questions buried in a lecture on Psychoanalysis: Where does a memory go when it is forgotten?

I did know that my younger self used to get off the train from Perugia or Bologna and walk the length of the long, grey platform beside the train, and then cross the shiny brown-and-beige-marbled floor and walk out towards the exit in front of the station to take a cab to Borgo Pinti, where she lived. But nothing in the station, or the stream whirling around me, looked familiar—no jolt to the memory box— nor did any sign or café awaken a long-lost memory or image. Nada.

In fact, even the café was new to me. The staff—all young women (it used to be middle-aged men) or foreigners—were dressed in white, with the name of the café stitched in blue above their shirt pockets. They looked interchangeable with youths working in fast-food joints back home.

The snacks in red-and-white wrappers, neatly stacked in front of the cashier and almost all of them filled with Nutella, also looked new. What happened to the rows and rows of wonderful fresh pastries and panni on display? There were some, and they did look delicious, but the sheer exuberant abundance was missing.

I boarded an empty train to Livorno and sat alone in the railway car. I waited for the conductor to arrive and check my ticket, but he never showed up. As the train pulled out of the station, I spotted the red-tiled dome of Santa Maria del Fiore, a.k.a. the famous *Il Duomo*, against an off-white-and-blue sky, and this is when it happened. A memory surfaced of going to the station one morning to meet Kay on her return to Florence. We embraced and kissed each other on both cheeks; nearby, a small gaggle of teenagers, some with pink streaks in their hair and others with blue, and all wearing red sneakers, gathered around each other, laughing and giggling on the platform like a conspiracy of clowns. We exited the station into the mid-morning light. It was early March and the light was bright and white and gave everything a sharp clarity; on the honey-brown, ancient walls it felt and looked like soft polished gold under the oval lights of a jeweller on Ponte Vecchio.

Near her apartment, on a quiet side street, grew a large leafy creeper dusted with purple-white flowers; it had grown and fanned across half the wall of the house. Part of the foliage was in the shade and looked a dull green while some of the other leaves were soaking up the warm, nutritious light and were a brilliant, bright green. It was a gorgeous surprise.

I had gone out for a walk without Kay for a cigarette and to parse her return; turned down an empty little alley I seldom walked on, paused to light a cigarette, exhaled, and looked up, and there in the light and shadow of the small alley I saw for the first time the pretty floral picture on the wall.

The wall creeper, along with the light that day, are now forever attached to Kay like an old song. There is something of a New Wave French film to that mental frame.

My memories here are almost all about light (my moody reflections about Kay and me, a short story elsewhere), and, of course, any artist worth his salt will tell you that is the essence of painting, and that how a painter deals with light is the essence of colour.

But you have to live in a place for at least a year, and see each season pass to the next, to see the corresponding change of light from one month to the next, how dark shades and types of light change week to week, month to month, into the next season.

Where you work as an artist, a painter in Modigliani's case, will affect how you use colour and, in turn, what ends up on the canvas. It is the authority of light.

Near the end of his life when he was ill on and off, Modigliani's mother, Eugénia, wrote to him to suggest he come home from Paris to recover. He replied he could not leave Paris; he no longer could paint in the light of Livorno.

"I do not know what I want. Perhaps it is nothing more than to live, dying slowly like a leaf," he replied.

Micheli's Art School, 1898

Amedeo Modigliani:
My bent was venereal from the beginning
When not painting nudes, preoccupied
With seducing the household maid
Unknown to my mother or my Aunt Laure
Shy, courteous, my body thin and frail after typhoid
Led me naturally to the passion of the flesh.
I quoted Nietzsche, D'Annunzio, Baudelaire
Fabulous tragic failures, true nobles of the spirit
So, they nicknamed me 'superman'
Even though I looked like Huck Finn
My short hair standing straight up.
My brother now a Socialist, mother a teacher, Aunt Laure: mad.
And I, an artist, entered Guglielmo Micheli's studio on the ground floor
Villa Baciocchi, a large cluttered room, easel, canvases,
Three windows and a paint-stained floor
Quiet ray of light in the morning
Still and burning cool, held the dust motes.
Natali, my school friend, proclaimed
I had 'a strange sense of superiority
And at the same time was a good companion.'
I already knew I wanted the café women of Paris,
Kiki of Montparnasse, La Quique, Fernande Oliver,
Before they existed,
Already knew if a woman poses for you
She gives herself to you
Already heard Marevna, my Russian mistress, painter, and model
Knock on my door, naked under her coat

Laugh, sit and sketch me, I told her:
'Drink to me with thine eyes and I will not look for wine.'
Ignored the Fattori style Micheli encouraged
But who influenced my carefully drawn line
And my lack of sympathy for full distortion
Wound of bourgeois decorum: a scar that never healed.

Modigliani and friends in Gino Romiti's Studio

In the photograph four young painters, gather around Gino Romiti, *Il Maestro*, who sits in the centre holding a square palette on his knee. On the palette there is a smudging cloth and three brushes sticking up, two on the palette and one in Romiti's hand. In front of them is a painting in progress of a well-dressed young man, standing. There is also a clearly distinguishable portrait of an older bourgeois man wearing a necktie. Several canvases lay scattered on the floor. The entire studio is shaded light and dark, in the manner of a Rembrandt painting, but probably more by accident than design.

Romiti, the oldest of the group and the teacher, sports a fine, pointed, dark goatee and on his upper lip a thick moustache parted in the middle. There are what appear to be white spots of paint on his painting jacket, but it is hard to say if it is paint or the photo was badly developed. Romiti is wearing a dark cravat that sits under his short, winged collar. He has gathered around him an atmosphere of gravitas. On his left is what looks like a waif of a boy, although in reality he is the same age as Modigliani, fourteen or fifteen. He is also wearing a tie—a proper little bourgeois—and his face is smooth, round, and impassive. Modigliani is on the right of the photo in the foreground, sitting beside Romiti, one of his hands placed affectionately on Romiti's shoulder. His entire posture and face exude confidence, the opposite of the waif-like boy. Behind Modigliani and Romiti stand two older, taller students. One of the two is well dressed and is caught staring intently away from the camera, arms crossed, at something funny in the studio. His eyes betray some kind of amusement at whatever he is looking at. The other student looks at the camera and appears to be in a bit of shock. His eyes are set wide in an oval face but expressionless and, like Modigliani, he is not wearing a tie. Modigliani's face looks resolute. His eyes look back at you and his face is uncompromising in attitude; his lips are firmly set, the bottom one full and sensuous. He holds his other hand inside his vest pocket like a confident banker. Modigliani looks sure of himself. Back straight, pants spattered with what seems to be white paint, but again, since it is a black-and-white photo, it is hard to say what colour the stains are, or if, in fact, his pants are paint stained.

Romiti and Modigliani are the only ones whose clothes seem to be stained with paint. No one in the photo is smiling, unless you include the ironic smirk of the tall one behind Romiti, and the alert eyes and slightly parted lips of *Il Maestro*.

Is it in this photo that you can see Modigliani, the artist, who loves the off note, who in Paris seeks and creates a booze-and-drug-fueled disorder? He defies whatever is fashionable, whatever carries the weight and freight of authority, quarrels with the Cubists, led informally by Picasso.

Modigliani is the only painter in Montparnasse who always carries half of a book of poetry in his velvet coat pocket (he would tear a book in half to make it portable) of Baudelaire, Lautréamont: transgressive, violent, and absurdist poets. His favorite poem is *The Albatross* by Baudelaire. It is a symbolic poem, and compares the fate of the poet (artist) to an albatross, mocked and crippled by crude sailors for sport. The albatross "outflies the tempest and laughs at the archer / Exiled aground amid jeers / His great wings prevent his walking." The poet/artist is wounded and mocked by indifference and incomprehension, suffers for his art and vision, even though he mocks his tormentors. Suffering is a wide umbrella for the lost and misfits and their lost causes. Even though the great albatross can fly, it is the symbol of the forsaken artist, its great wings, (spirit), marked and clipped by neglect.

Modigliani in Paris is the scorned albatross: his great, wounded, romantic spirit fuels his self-destructive impulse, part of his disdain for one and all, yet yearning for...?

Today in the photograph he is merely posing (forever), the portrait of a young teenager as an artist. Did he ever stop posing? Did he ever get clear of his bourgeoise upbringing?

1901

Eugénia Modigliani:
All artists, great or not, have a mother.
I worry about the lesion on his lung
Left after typhoid fever, his recent relapse.
He returned to me a spoiled boy,
Lively, intelligent, and a found sense of destiny.
I worry about his pale complexion, money.
Today he sits like a dull, white, smoldering coal.
Despondent, he says in perfect French: 'Livorno
Does not have the right category of painters, people.'
He forgives my frown in two quick invisible strokes
Traced in the air in the shape of a head,
Smiles the irrepressible smile of a man who
Waits to see the tender grey sea in first light after lovemaking.
'Seriously,' he says, 'how can the pursuit of Art destroy you?'
There it is again: the Garson sense of irony.
I decide he will spend the winter in the south for his health.

Part Two: Italian Days

Modigliani wrote a series of letters from Southern Italy to his older friend, painter Oscar Ghiglia, and later wrote again from Rome, Florence, Venice.

The letters describe Modigliani's attempt to explore and define himself as an artist. Both Modigliani and Ghiglia were trying to escape the limitations and provincialism of the Livorno art scene, led primarily by Micheli, their former teacher and a student of Fattori, one of the leaders of the Macchiaioli Movement, a precursor of Impressionism.

Villa Bitter, Ana Capri, Island of Capri, 1901

Dear Oscar,
Capri, the very name stirs a tumult of images
Beauty, ancient sensuality
Voluptuous sea and mountains.
The English everywhere here hold a red Baedeker,
Strange, exotic and venomous flower to avoid at all costs.
Yesterday I went for a walk under the moon, scent of oranges
Alone with a Norwegian girl.
You could hear the applause of the sea on the stone steps
Hear it roll tender against the shore
Wave after wave, sigh after sigh, again and again
The way I wanted to make love to this girl.
Enough poetry
I write to take a moment with you
Rejoice in your success in Venice
Tell you I believe in your alteration after Florence
And unlike you I cannot follow Micheli after Fattori far.
After four months I have brought nothing to conclusion
I accumulate material, work at English
Soon I will go to Rome, then Venice for the Exposition
Sea this morning makes a deep inhuman sound
Fishermen toss nets and catch the sun for a moment
Is this what I am trying to do,
Toss and abandon myself to find myself?
Greet Vinzio.
—Ciao, Dedo

Florence, Italy, 1901

Dear Dedo,
Your enthusiasm, energy, desire for lucidity I admire
But I advise you to guard
Against the splintering and diffusion of your energy.
You write you wish to be a rich, abundant river
Spread joy over the land
To find the truth about life and art.
Your heart soars like a bird above the ground, sings generosity
Claims the future and rights different from other people.
Pure Nietzsche, your old friend, or is it Raskolnikov?
You struggle to separate and find your own
Thoughts, feelings and beliefs from the accepted norms,
To place aesthetic needs above human duty.
You have marked well the boundaries in which an artist must live
But the quest for beauty is always tragic, inevitably invites disappoint-
ment.
Our meanings cannot be nor will they ever be bourgeois meanings
To question is to walk with nothing under your feet and no God
above your head.
I do not wish to tell you the precise cause or reason for my suffering
Only that the remedy is the will to work.
Forgive Fattori, the lines in his paintings are intelligent
The movement of line, precise.
I admire clarity, cold clean art.
His subjects once ignored are now found on framed canvas.
Continue to dream, my friend, my brother.
—Affectionately, Oscar

Hotel Pagano, Capri, 1901

Dear Ghiglia,

Yes, yes, I did visit some of the seedy streets of Livorno—my God the stench—(I wish I knew how to paint it), and painted the humble oxen and cart, poor but noble barefooted children and walked and painted outside the city with Natalie. But, I believe art comes from art and not nature. Micheli tells us, as Fattori taught him, "Paint what is." But, what in fact does this mean? A painting can never be absolutely true to what is real in nature, be nature's equal. I want to paint the live human form, the nude in the studio or portrait and ignore all this fuss about subject matter and painting en plein air, to capture natural light and shadow.

I foresee the time when I shall settle, probably at Florence, and work in the best sense of the word and apply myself with faith, head and body, to organize and develop all the impressions, all the ideas I have accumulated in this mystic garden. I too still search for answers but your obligation is to save your dream.

I want to talk to you about the difference between the work of the artist who communes with nature and the one who educates himself in the studio, in the republic of art. I want to live separate and pure, find an art worth pursuing.

Does one enjoy himself in Livorno?

—M

Livorno Diary #2: Divertimento a Livorno

I ask myself a similar question as the empty train speeds towards Livorno: what is there to do in Livorno? Nevertheless, I do have a concrete mission: to visit Casa Modigliani at 38 Via Roma where Modigliani was born, and after, see if I can find the two other former family residences, one on Piazza Magenta, and the final home on Via Cambini. The rest I leave to organized speculation and fate, perhaps collect some Livorno atmosphere.

It is near the end of October and remarkably sunny, and the countryside is still a solid green. The train zips past the backside of small, bland, industrial factories; long, white, two-storey office buildings with red, ceramic-tiled roofs; parking lots facing the railway tracks; and assorted farming equipment parked near small gardens with lean cornstalks and vegetables of some kind in a row. Now and again, a road appears with trucks and cars set back but parallel with the train tracks.

Contrary to the general stereotype, Italy, at least in the North, is well ordered and neat from the vantage point of a train.

The landscape flickers by briskly and changes from moment to moment under a spotless blue sky. After about twenty minutes, the air gets noticeably warmer, and by the time we get to the Livorno station, it feels hot.

My journey starts off on the wrong flat-foot when I turn incorrectly in the pedestrian tunnel that runs under the station. I had walked up stairs that emerged into a vacant lot with a fence around it and a few old cars belonging, my guess, to workers at the station.

Back down the stairs, I walk the other way and exit at the front of the station. There is no one about except for the barista and his helper, and a ticket agent inside his cluttered office. In the bar, a few tattooed high school students are sitting at two tables smoking and drinking soft drinks with straws. One of the group is restless and moves from one table to the other and back again. I think for a moment she is high. Their ennui feels contagious. We glance and ignore each other in the four steps it takes me to walk by their table.

I exit the station bar and in seconds there is a cab driver waving me towards his car. He is thin and tall, wears sunglasses and a blue golf shirt (ah, the Italian attachment and fascination bordering on fetish with the colour blue), and is a friendly and helpful fellow. He opens the car door and once inside I ask:

—How is life in Livorno?

—*Qui si sta bene* (things are good here).

—Well, you have great weather.

—Yes, this year marvellous. They got a deluge the other day in Rome, but nothing but clear sky here, ha, ha.

I look out the window. The light is clear, an off-white; the opposite of my memory of the light of Paris in the fall. I mention this to the cabdriver.

He shrugs.

—The air is colder and damp in Paris.

I ask him if he has heard of the painter Modigliani.

—Yes, everyone claims a piece of him. The tourist board, shops, even the politicians. I am not sure in what neighbourhood he used to live.

I let it slip I am here to do research for a book that I hope to write about Modigliani, absorb some Livorno atmosphere.

—The atmosphere is better in the summer. Everyone from Florence is here and goes to the beach. Many cruise ships arrive, or people take the ferry to Sardinia. The city is alive. Dead, this time of year. Few tourists and fewer chances to make money.

He does not seem very interested or curious about my writing project.

—Are you French? From Rome? Your accent, well, is classic. You don't hiss your Cs like the people from Tuscany.

I recall this odd little quirk, about the way people in Tuscany pronounce their Italian Cs, from my time spent in Florence many years ago.

—I am from Canada. A long way from here. What kind of accent do I have?

—Ah, Canada. Wonderful country, like Norway. It is my dream to see live polar bears. I watch them on TV. Don't worry, your Italian is very good. I wish I could speak English the way you speak Italian.

After a series of twists and turns we are finally on Via San Jacopo in Aqua Vita and approaching the B&B I booked. It is on a small two-lane road; a narrow sidewalk hugs the edges of the houses that sit cheek by jowl.

The sun is up but the homes follow the odd angle of the street, so most of the road is covered in grey shadow even though it is only late morning. I discover later, to my delight and surprise, that further up the street is the Giovanni Fattori Museum in the Villa Mimbelli.

Our conversation about Italian accents is interrupted by a phone call. The cab driver's phone ringer is the theme music for *The Game of Thrones* (*Il Gioco di Troni*). He is a fan.

After the call he says:

—Tonight is a full moon. Walk down to Terrazza Mascagni around midnight and you will hear the tide come in. Look out at the ships' lights at sea. Magical. Take in the sea air. Dream you are a pirate in our port and she waits for you in Caffè Bardi. What to do in Livorno? What a question! It is October on a Monday night—go and watch TV in the bar, ha ha. We have arrived. Look, there is your B&B.

Venice, 1903

*"I want to sculpture... great, grandiose statues...receive
immense commissions..."*
Modigliani to Ortiz de Zarate, Chilean painter

In Naples and Florence, I discovered Tino di Camaino's
Gothic spiritual faces:
Alert and bewildered Battista, Christ's aroused Grace,
Hope's ache and longing, Faith delicate and pure.
Poetry in stone is a kind of purity.
Tino is a true believer:
Real faces, elegant and humble.
You can feel his calm, spiritual agitation,
The clean rhythmic line, organized volume.
I want to create monuments
Like Michelangelo, it is my destiny.
I have seen the marble quarry at Mount Altissimo,
His room by the communal clock in Pietrasanta,
Retraced his steps in the piazza.
I wear the same unadorned nobility of spirit.

The artist before and after Venice: Amedeo Modigliani
   ** Rodin must be opposed. He is eminent. (after)
   ** I am suspicious of the subconscious. What can it teach you? Show? (after)
   ** A nude model differs from a nude painting in that the painting always waits for love.
   ** Beatrice Hastings—the femme fatale with the long cigarette holder—is neither a saint   nor a sinner but merely a bad poet and eccentric lover. (after)
   ** I admire Lautréamont's *Les Chants de Maldoror*. They are the creation of a mad intoxicated genius who uses disorientation to break down the narrow walls of morality. (before)
   ** The most important rule is in my heart, not theory. Art should touch a chord in the heart, resonate, and excite our intelligence. (before)
   ** I require a living model in front of me. Abstraction exhausts and kills. (after)
   ** I fall in and out of love with D'Annunzio's work at least once a week, yes to passion, revulsion at his decadent tastes. (before)
   ** Influences: from Naples, the sculptor Tino di Camaino, shape of eyes, balance of volume on a head. Capri: sensuous enigmatic Etruscan smiles. Rome: elegant ancient capital fixed on seven hills, tragic grandeur, feverish and sweet. I admire her grace, her melancholy and beauty at dawn. (before)
   ** Misurina: a village near the Dolomites Mountains. I came here to inhale the pure mountain air (for my poor weak lungs), see Titan's blue (he is from here), study his nudes. (before)
   **Influence is awakened desire. The tides of beauty rise and fall in Venice under a full moon. (before)
   ** Venice: There I discovered my taste for hashish and lovemaking. Giudecca is the flesh-pot of Venice. (before)
   ** An aristocracy of feeling and noble purpose separates me from

the common man; this is what makes an artist. My taste in fine clothes, my attraction to and desire for many lovers, and above all the will to live alive and in opposition to rules does not discount my kindness.

** "Socialism," my brother Emmanuelle and his friends are fond of saying, "is the cheese on the macaroni." Bald-headed parrots, each of them, but I do respect my brother's generous intelligence and taste. (before and after)

** This last sentence (No. 14) is superfluous. I am superstitious (the oculist in me) as everyone knows, ha ha ha.

Venice, 1903

Before enrolling in the Scuola Libera di Nudo, The School of Nude Studies, Accademia delle Belle Arti in Venice, Modigliani checks into an expensive apartment on Via 22 Maggio. It is near the Piazza San Marco, the most beautiful drawing room in all of Europe, according to Napoleon Bonaparte.

It is midmorning. He wants to walk the full length of the S-shaped Grand Canal, take in the ephemeral sights and sounds, see the impossible neo-Gothic palazzi and churches built right up to the canal's edge so that they seem to float. He wants to see the delicate, gauzy mix of light and water on the lagoon at midday; see the Doge's Palace stone Gothic windows and arches, airy and ethereal at twilight.

He knows about the city's sights, the play of light on water. The Gothic mirages on water, an inspiration to so many painters centuries before him and today.

Modigliani is on stage at the top of the Rialto bridge, watching black, shiny gondolas move towards him, guided by the steady push and pull of the gondoliers on their poles. He notes how the black ribbons at the back of their round, large hats are tossed by a new spring breeze. One gondola in particular catches his eye. In it are two young, pretty, blonde women, probably German, he guesses. One looks serious and wears awe-inspired anxiety on her face, while the other wears a perpetual grin, her round, clear, blue, Botticelli eyes sparkling with glee. In an allegoric Renaissance painting, he thinks one face would be the simple, pious Virgin Mary shocked by a visit from the Archangel Gabriel, and the other face Venus born and rising from the sea with an ironic, detached smile.

Modigliani walks the streets in new, smart, immaculate clothes bought in Rome. He is refined but not showy, wears a thick, black wool overcoat that casually sits on his shoulders, and on his head a black felt Trilby hat with a wide band, on his hands brown lamb-skin gloves. Under his coat are tailored, black, pinstriped pants and jacket, a warm grey sweater (it is spring), and a crisp white shirt. On his shirt collar sits a small, discreet, solid black necktie.

Modigliani in costume cuts a fine bourgeois figure, with a hint of flirty danger.

He waits until they are close enough for him to see the shape of their necks, and then raises his hat and shouts down from the bridge. "*Buongiorno, signorine*" (good morning, ladies), and smiles his famous impish smile, dark eyes blazing and intense. He knows women find him attractive and he enjoys creating the illusion, the aura, that under his clothes hides a Greek god.

To his surprise it is the serious virgin who smiles and waves at him with her guidebook in her hand and shouts, "*Buongiorno, signore.*" He salutes her by lifting his hat again and shouts "*Caffè Florian alle quattro del pomeriggio*" (Caffè Florian at four in the afternoon), as the gondola begins to slip under the bridge. He thinks this could be interesting, but it is a roll of the dice—they may or may not meet—but, nevertheless, he is pleased she waved back, and with himself.

Modigliani 's expensive apartment off Piazza San Marco is paid for by his wealthy Uncle Amedeo, but shortly after, he moves to humble quarters more fitting for a penniless student. Modigliani enjoys the grand gesture, even if it is theatrical and short-lived. He will later do the same when he arrives in Paris in 1906 and on first arrival takes up residence in the elegant Madeleine district before Picasso suggests he move to less expensive and artistic Montparnasse.

He is ecstatic to be in Venice. He later writes to Oscar: "From Venice…the most precious inspirations of my life; Venice, Medusa-headed of countless blue serpents, sea eye immense green in which the spirit loses itself and is exalted toward the infinite…"

From Naples he brings to Venice a new-found love, sculpture; an exuberant poetic spirit informed by Nietzsche, Baudelaire; and a re-born and passionate sense of destiny as an artist. The gift of prophecy. But he is far from the disorderly, romantic rebel he later becomes in Paris.

Today is his first day in Venice.

Giudecca nights: The Joys of Spiritualism and Hashish, Venice, 1904

My friends are the painters Guido Marussig, Mario Crepet, Cesare Mainella, Arengo Soffici, Umberto Boccioni, Futurist painter and sculptor. I live with Fabio Maurone, who is interested in everything: sculpture, painting, engraving, graphic arts, and art criticism. We all meet at the Caffè Florian to watch foreign girls from the corners of our eyes, and discuss and discuss. I care little for discussions about art. I enjoy their company.

I visit churches and brothels and eat hashish, primarily with Guido Cardorin, at gatherings run by a Neapolitan aristocrat called Cuccolo, on the island of Giudecca.

Cardorin and I cross over to Giudecca from the Accademia where Cuccolo waits for us at night. We are silent except for the gentle slap of water against the rowboat, but we can barely contain our excitement. When our eyes meet, we give each other a nervous smile. We can see lit candles in the windows of the convents, hospitals, and homes. Here and there, the water is stained by gold-and-yellow lantern light. The gold light simmers on the water and it feels as if we are in a fairy tale, crossing a dark green and blue sea. We listen for the sound of Giudecca's many church bells to guide our direction.

Cuccolo, or Croccolo, is short, and his plump body bears some resemblance to Napoleon's. He always dresses in grey, and cuts a fine, elegant figure. Cuccolo finds and provides Cardorin and me with two local girls who live on Giudecca Island. They are part of the long Venetian tradition of providing entertainment and sharing female assets with real gentlemen. I pay a small price. Cuccolo only asks to watch through a peephole. He asks to make sure my girl wears a belt with small bells around her waist. I do not know where the peephole is, nor do I hear him, but after, he always returns my smile with an ironic smile of his own and a wistful sigh.

Tonight she has powdered her anus and rouged her nipples with a soft, rose-pink, edible paste; it is sweet marzipan freckled with small bits of bitter green hashish. Her areolae are painted a bright red, as are her bottom outer lips. She parts her small lips; the soft pink just past her dark pubic hair matches the colour of the paste on her nipples. In anticipation of my request from my last visit, she wears a belt around her waist studded with several small bells. A tiny gold medallion falls and rests just above her pubic mound. Her white alabaster skin is freshly bathed and scented. She pirouettes for me. Her white skin glows in the candlelight: a flawless, white marble statue suddenly alive.

She kneels in front of me like an archangel without massive wings. Her eyes watch me intently as she playful applies the paste with both hands. Her strokes are slow, gentle. I rise. We both smile and her smile is irresistible, so I bend forward and kiss her. We soon enter each other's kingdom, one kiss at a time, until we turn into a wheel and taste each other, devour, on each end. I catch her rhythm. A current of pleasure runs between us. The bells ring softly as she moves deliberately up and slowly down. She moves faster with each stroke until she shudders in my arms, bells proclaiming her release. Her eyes shine with pleasure, sparkle above me like stars.

After a refreshing bath and a snack, including coffee, we all gather to use Tarot cards to announce the future, and later a "Spiritual Board" to try to contact the long-lost dead. The séances feel less morbid after we have taken our pleasure rather than before. Our mood and touch is playful as we wait to hear about our wish for contact, any word or gesture, from the dead. The girls laugh easily, and my charm and well-timed flattery breaks the strain of pursuing spirits. The ladies are relaxed and happy in our company in spite of my own perverse delight in exhibitionism, which I gladly share with Cucculo.

On the boat ride back to Venice, Cardorin questions me as if possessed by fervour.

—What is this spiritual need of yours? Your gift of prophecy? What madness! I am complicit and uncomfortable. Cucculo is a fine fellow, but I would never allow him to watch me. A strange pleasure you share with him, Dedo. Strange and odd evening, asking questions, seeking knowledge of the past and future from cards, from the spirits of the dead, he says.

I can still feel the effects of the hashish, and hum a little tune instead of answering him, watch the distance lights on the Caffè Florian awning expand and contract, dance, shatter, and shine like jewels. Cardorin stares at me as if he is in a boat with the devil himself.

I close my eyes and place two coins on my eye sockets. The silence between us vaguely uncomfortable.

—Look Cardorin, I am one of the dead and we are crossing the River Styx.

I laugh, and he now laughs, and then I tilt my head forward and the coins fall off my face and make a small dull thud at the bottom of the rowboat.

—There. A small tip for the ferryman who will soon take me across. Payment for the permission the noble pursuit of art grants. Never forget, Cardorin, an artist is superior.

Cardorin shudders in response.

Modigliani, the Sun, planets and some stars

Your chart shows Virgo rising as your first house. This makes it your ruling planet or, as our ancestors referred to it, the "star" one is born under, Mercury or Hermes. The sign Virgo is ruled by Mercury. In the mystical Qabala, Mercury is connected to the orb or sephiroth HOD, which is associated with Mercury, your leading planet. (HOD is one of the ten sephiroth or orbs in the Quabla tree.)

It is the sphere of the mental faculties, namely imagination and intelligence, and, owing to Mercury's dualistic character, it also has an evil side—reason and logic—which we occultists distrust.

Concerning your visual artistic works and lifestyle, you have in your chart Mercury, an exact conjunct to Venus. This is an indication of artistic pursuits, and, in this case, expression through painting. This planetary placement of Mercury and Venus—the planet Venus's energies reputably artistic—are further entrenched by the joining of the Sun, giving a stellum (a grouping of planets) of these three orbs. There is in your chart a powerful, interactive stellum concerning your artistic-creative life.

Art encompasses the urgent need of expression. Astrology is, on the other hand, an occult pursuit and one of the four branches of MaGick. The occult concerns the hidden investigations underneath common senses. Within this esoteric tradition lie the elements of symbolism, psychic phenomena, metaphysics, tantric and nature observances, to name a few. In the Arts, public expression is the key.

To understand any phenomenon or creative person's life, one needs to understand the concurrent time. Your style emerges from many cultural feeds. Your exquisite use of line and muted colours, and your portraits and female nudes, will make a lasting imprint on Western painting.

You are drawn (pardon the pun) to the spiritual and preternatural and the ever-elusive muse depicted in your stylized portraits of *pulpeuse* (luscious) females.

Astrologically, your Sun sign is Cancer. Most mediums and seers are born under the Sun sign Cancer. Cancer artists/painters have a fluid type of treatment of shapes and colours different than, let's say, a Gemini with a linear graphic and nucleic and concentrated depiction.

Your star chart shows the gift of Mercury (Virgo rising) with its graphic linear sensibilities plus the sensitivity of water-based emotive expression. Also contributing to your creativity in painting is your known tempestuous and extreme bohemian lifestyle. We find the planet Mars conjunct Uranus sitting in your first house of self-expression. This denotes a textbook definition in astrology of an explosive and often belligerent outward incursion into the world. You will not go out of your way, Signore Modigliani, to avoid any altercation.

Part Three: Paris Days

Café Tales, Paris, Café de la Rotonde, 1915

Amedeo Modigliani:

This story is a good laugh, and you, my friends of the demimonde, love a good, naughty story, do you not? I don't care if you have heard it before! It is enough that it pleases me. A magical story of seduction, a comedy of manners. What could be better? And it proves I am an incurable lover, ha ha.

Beatrice, I can see you frown. Smile my love.

Now I ask, pay close attention, whisper if you must talk. The roar and buzz in here tonight is too much. Waiter, can you tell that table over there to stop talking so loudly? Yes, the woman with the black hat and feather, smoking, and her man of the evening.

Beatrice, can you for once find a place for the ducklings in your basket and, dearest, don't look so cross. We are all artists here tonight, and after a long day of struggle wish to spend a gay evening together.

Yes, of course, I agree; on with the story…enough of my prologue. My intention is not to invent a story but to glorify the event.

Let me set the scene:

I was on my way here to this lovely emporium of art, ruined temple to beauty, ah Paris, from Venice, the green serpent's eye on the blue sea, via prosperous Geneva. Smartly dressed. Impeccable manners. I cut the figure of the perfect gentleman.

Now, we all know the ancient gods favoured chance, a portal, and what did chance bring that day on the platform but a well-dressed mother, about forty, and her young, pretty daughter of approximately seventeen or sixteen but claiming her age of innocence was over and gave herself the age of eighteen. I would learn this later.

Mother and daughter were well put together: fashionable coats and shawls and in season, and both possessed fine features—pretty grey-blue eyes (like Athena), high, delicate cheekbones, figures shaped like flutes.

The mother's eyes and mine met and we exchanged pleasantries regarding the weather and our hopes for a safe and comfortable journey. She no doubt noted my finery and asked what was the purpose of my visit to Paris.

I flattered her in kind, and soon enough we both decided it would be a lovely way to pass the time on a dull train trip if we did so together in amiable conversation. So, she invited me to their train compartment. I settled in and sat across from the two lovelies.

I smile at what happened next. The mother, I am certain, enjoyed my idle compliments, my discrete comments. I mentioned the lovely rose-water scent in the compartment, and she explained it was that very morning that she had squirted the scent from a spritzer made of thick cut glass and adorned with a purple tassel (purple, of course, the colour of passion).

"How charming, Madame," I gushed, "misty delight inside a firm container." I continued, "You are a woman of impeccable taste." She blushed with approval. I mentioned how satin feels against the skin; "although the cost can be prohibitive, the feeling, nevertheless, is worth it. Can you recommend a shop in Paris, Madame?"

This kind of thing continued on and off for a few hours. She clearly had been well schooled in the ministry of coquet and enjoyed our sallies into the gentle sea of *amour courtois*. I, on the other hand, pretended to enjoy our tête-à-tête and acted the part of a gay, honourable gallant. The daughter all the while feigned reading her book, but throughout my conversation our eyes would meet and she would smile and I would smile, but Mama assumed the smile was for her eyes only. Or I would give the daughter a quick wink when her mother turned to adjust herself, and the finest pink-and-white blush would rise, and her eyes dance with merry amusement. At one point she placed her right hand down and waited for the right moment, and then slowly lifted her middle finger until it was vertical and asked if I felt the heat of the day rise. "Indeed, I do, Mademoiselle, we must be directly above Nice," I replied. Her little nod of approval at my remark and discreet smile was heaven-sent—and right under the nose, so to speak, of her mother. I formed a deliberate and slow smile, and she nodded again and then moved her hand and placed it on her lap and cupped her hand around her middle finger. She smiled and pushed her head back as if resting for a moment, darted a quick glance of disapproval at her mother, and then tapped herself with her open palm just below her neck and, unknown to her mother, flashed a quick and wide mischievous grin.

Imagine my secret surge. The pleasures of ironic and covert seduction!

Modesty prevents me from telling you more. Your roars of approval tell me you are enjoying my saucy little tale—do not pardon the pun. No, I will not tell you the shape of her tits. I am a gentleman and, what's more, this is a public gathering. How tight was it? Please sir, I am shocked at such a question. I am an artist and so are you, Jean… ha ha ha, right you are, all false modesty.

Suffice to say, she was, and I assume still is, a beautiful filly. I regret never learning their address. I can attest to the fact that her legs are beautiful, sculpted; the shape of her derriere round and flawless as an egg. Perfect.

Give us a smile, Beatrice. You also brag about your lovers…never in public, true. You look cross, like her mother, but ho ho ho, her mother never suspected a thing. I politely took my leave from them at the Gare de l'Est, tipped my hat in salute, and goodbye. Mama was breathless, bemused in the end and somewhat rueful, but she kept her dignity, silly bourgeois. What a deuce of a woman! I left the daughter, a tender colt ready to ride another stranger. She cooed her goodbye. The End. Ha ha ha.

There, much better, Beatrice—laugh. Our lives are already tragic.

*

Roger Wild (French artist) describes Modigliani's grand entry at the Rotonde, how he would cast a glance around and mimic various artists, ironically, in a sign of greeting: "*Delhay, crapaud!* (Delhay, toad!) Soutine, have you bathed? Mon Dieu, you stink!"

Wild is now seventy-eight and sits at a table framed in a window, construction on rue de Sevres behind his head. His wife sits beside him on a piano stool.

As a young man, Wild heard Modigliani strike the tabletop as he recited Dante, fingertips pounding out the metre. His wife leaned forward and said, "That's Modigliani's voice, you know." My blood ran cold. "Can you do that again?" He began to recite—a deep voice with a hard, grinding edge; a sound both resonant and strangled.

Livorno Diary #3: The Caterpillar asks Alice

I was first attracted to Modigliani when I came across a matted post-card-sized print of one of his nudes in a bookstore in Vancouver. The small print was on the bookshelf in the poetry section. I was instantly taken by the lush orange colour and dark eyes, the beautiful full figure, and natural or casual way the nude lay stretched out on the divan. It was a beautiful image, even in miniature. I looked on the back of the card and noted the name was Italian. This added to his allure and tweaked my curiosity further. At the time I was still looking for mentors for artistic or creative direction, and here was a fellow Italian who might prove interesting and useful. I went over to the art book section and, lo and behold, there were two coffee table books of his works. I pulled one out at random. I don't recall the curator of the book, and I am not sure it is even in print today. Besides the nudes, the book included a vast assortment of his portraits, many of them with what I later learned are his characteristic elongated necks. There were photos of several of his head sculptures that looked more like masks than faces. Looking at the portraits triggered a memory from a time when I was consuming the works of John Fowles and of the main character in the short story *The Ebony Tower*, an artist, who talks about Modigliani's necks and how his nudes could never have been painted by an Englishman. The remark must have stuck, mainly because it suggested some kind of inner understanding about the repressive ways of English culture and how, of course, as an artist he resists and resents sexual repression.

So, some thirty-plus years later, I am in Livorno, or "Leghorn," the place from where the early 19th century Romantic English poet Shelley set out to sail to Lerici, a town north and up the coast from here. He drowned in an unexpected sea storm in what was later reported by his wife, Mary Shelley, early feminist and author of

Frankenstein, due to the faulty construction of the boat.

All three—Shelley, Modigliani, and Fowles' spokesman in *The Ebony Tower*, Henry Breasley—rebelled against sexual repression and hypocritical pieties.

Modigliani's reason for leaving Livorno as a young teenager, on the surface, was to help him recover from his pleurisy, and to study art in Capri, Rome, Florence, and Venice. But what is clear from reading his letters to Ghiglia, his older artist friend, is he was also trying to cobble together a vision of himself as an artist, to find himself as an artist. He understood this meant looking beyond current artistic trends and discovering his own artistic models, slowly articulating what was meaningful to him as a young man, as an artist, both in subject matter and medium. His letters also hint at a desire for sexual adventure.

The letters show him under the sway of poetry: the sentences in his letters are often poetic and reach to be evocative and descriptive. He also has literally absorbed Nietzsche's aesthetics: "For art to exist, for any aesthetic activity or perception to exist, a certain physiological precondition is indispensable: intoxication."

Modigliani's life, attitudes, and work habits in Paris articulate this point of view. He drinks from demi-glasses small sips of absinthe—as he paints, and by the time he has completed the first sitting, he is drunk.

The Dionysian vision reorganizes and alters perceptions, releases creative energy. The Apollonian (rationality) vision—produces 'reason's sleep,' to quote Blake— and is a dead end when it comes to being an artist according to this view.

Modigliani begins to experiment with drugs in Venice, and drugs and alcohol end up dominating the remaining fourteen years of his life in Paris. He self-consciously transforms himself, and sees himself, like earlier French Romantic poets did, as one of the artistic *maudit* (cursed). Modi—Modigliani's nickname in Paris—is a pun on the French word.

Modigliani was a great reader, and loved poetry, in particular. His taste and admiration for poets such as Baudelaire and Lautréamont suggests a young man who wants to lead his own internal revolution, overthrow learned conventions, comforts, and pleasures of a middle-class life; someone who wishes to escape sexual convention and morality. Modigliani views art as holy (like the Beats) and the artist as a saint as he struggles to be true to himself and his art, to live as he pleases. The only way to live is as a pure artist—consequences, social judgments, and health be damned.

Modigliani's starting point (and mine) is Livorno. From an early age, he wanted to visit the Uffizi Gallery in Florence, leave the provincial art scene of Livorno.

I am here in Livorno tonight, and hope to discover in the next few days something from Modigliani's past, find traces of what he left behind almost a hundred years ago. I realize it is a bit of a shaman's journey, attaching importance or something magical to the places people lived or objects they used every day. I am uncertain what I will find, if anything.

The only thing I am certain about this evening is my desire for dinner. I even distrust my ability to follow my iPhone's direction to the Osteria del Mare, the seafood restaurant I have chosen. It is dark. The phone glowing in my hand makes it obvious I am a tourist.

Modigliani's new starting point back in 1902-3 was sculpting, and he proceeded with amazing certainty, and then switched to painting. My starting point is here, in this small room with a pen noiselessly moving across the white space between the blue lines, uncertain if this trip to Livorno will produce any writing or insight.

The street is silent when I step out; no one is around. "Therefore, nobody walks faster than you," said the hookah-smoking (hashish?) caterpillar to Alice in *Alice in Wonderland*.

Leaving Venice, 1906

Amedeo Modigliani:

"All of Italy, if not Europe itself, with the exception of Paris, is provincial regardless of the pinpricks by Baudelaire or Nietzsche, or the hashish-eating avant-garde such as D'Annunzio."

So says Ortiz de Zárate, my Chilean painter friend and fellow hashish eater in Venice. I enjoy his irony. Laugh. End-to-end smile crosses his large wrestler face (worthy of sculpture), pleased with himself and his ironic comment. He continues:

"Your purpose is to be on guard and against complacent, stilted morality, proper culture, institutions, and politics. Only the artist is a free man."

I have been told he once clubbed his wife with a cake of yellow soap, asserting his freedom.

"Could not agree with you more, dear Ortiz."

I do not tell him I am like the canals of Venice: on the surface I am calm and placid, shy, but underneath me run deep, strong, unseen and dangerous currents.

Before leaving Venice at the end of 1905, my mother paid me a visit and gave me a copy of the British poet Oscar Wilde's *The Ballad of Reading Gaol*, and a small sum of money for travelling and living expenses in Paris. What am I to make of her choice of gift: an English poet? "You destroy what you love most," says Wilde. Am I destroying her?

I sold my brushes and paint to my roommate Fabio Mauroner. My future is sculpture, written in stone, so to speak.

To arrive in Paris is to be born again as an artist.

Click-clack, click-clack, click-clack, don't look back, train to Paris and a new hat, click-clack, train to Paris, don't look back.

Paris, end of January 1906, Boyish Charm

When Modigliani first arrived in Paris, he took a series of hotel rooms on the Right Bank. I think he even spent a few nights at the luxurious Hotel Scribe, between Gaumont Opéra and La Madeleine and a short fifteen-minute walk to The Louvre, before moving to Montmartre.

He cut the figure of a discriminating and cultured and proper, but colourful bourgeois gentleman-painter much like he did in Venice: wide black hat, red scarf and belt, scarlet-lined cape on the shoulders, loose checkered shirt.

Shy, well-dressed, he disdained the proletarian bohemian dress of blue overalls favoured by his fellow artists he met up with at La Lapin Agile. After meeting Picasso, he remarked, "He may have talent, but that is a poor excuse to dress badly."

His proper attire did not distract from his sweetness of expression and grace. He was lively in the half-dark of the La Lapin Agile, an energetic and enthusiastic conversationalist, and it is noted how oddly well-informed he was about occult matters. Modigliani, although shy, was not self-conscious. He leans into the conversation whenever the topic turned to women, hashish, morphine, opium (the novel *Black Opium* by Claude Farrère, recently published in 1904).

He exuded a boyish charm. The Russian-born sculptor, Ossip Zadkine, called him "a young god masquerading as a workman in his Sunday best." Others remarked on his noble features, his beautiful Roman head and jet-black hair, soulful eyes, and wry smile.

Modigliani, after a several weeks, moved and rented a studio on rue Caulaincourt in Montmartre. It was the beginning of his transformation from courtly, bourgeois gentleman to damned, soulful, and penniless, drug-addicted artist.

Picasso advised Modigliani, "Now, quit your smart hotel. The pensione that you chose is fine for painting flowers, but painters who are real have no damn business stuck so near the Madeleine."

On rue Caulaincourt, in 1904, there still existed wild, dense scrub wood on one side of the street, and on the other a series of shacks and squatters' homes. The area resembled a makeshift, third-world village rather than the urbane 18th arrondissement it is today.

Rue Caulaincourt was a wasteland, a vacant lot pitted and filled here and there with trash. The land was once quarried for stone for the building of Sacre Coeur Cathedral.

Modigliani lived in a shack, complete with corrugated iron roof, stolen bricks and glass, a door made of boards, all held together with wire and overgrown vines. He furnished his "apartment" with a makeshift cot; on the wall beside the bed were some postcards of early and late Italian Renaissance painters: Duccio di Buoninsegna(*Madonna and Child*, 1308) Vittore Carpaccio (*Dream of St. Ursula*, 1495) Simone Martini (*Virgin, Child, and Saints*, 1321). The post-cards suggest a painter interested (or, at the very least, one who ap-proves) in balance and vivid colour and realism when it comes to how the human face and body are represented. The painters were in-fluential seeds, first hinted at in his letters from Rome; they would eventually bloom and contribute to his future rejection of Cubism. The fact that the postcards had religious themes also suggests Modigliani was no knee-jerk atheist.

The room's furniture included two rush-bottomed chairs, one with its back broken, and a small, black wooden trunk for a table. And, regardless of his financial situation, there was always a zinc tub and a ceramic water jug present.

He would end a painting session dripping in sweat and would imme-diately bathe. It was not ablution for the sin of art but rather fastidi-ousness. He was the most fastidious of all the artists in Paris. A very peculiar bohemian.
—Lunia Czechowska

Livorno Diary #4: A Proper Gentleman

Livorno is a big, noisy creation compared to the relative calm and unobtrusive town of Cesena. The streets are lined with big, long apartment blocks, six to eight storeys high, one after another, with balconies, green shutters beside windows, and, in some cases, crumbling exteriors. In some neighbourhoods, laundry hangs on the edge of the balconies. The apartment blocks are not all new buildings. I imagine the lifts in some are not working, or perhaps their function is spotty, and the result is the painful inconvenience of carrying groceries up six flights of stairs under the glow of a dim lightbulb. Their exteriors are a pink/rose colour, or white/grey, and crumbling. This is especially true of a series of apartment blocks I encountered on the edges of the park, Villa Regina, on my way to Osteria del Mare, the restaurant suggested by my iPhone.

I am walking from my B&B, chosen online. It is run by an Italian American woman and her son who chose to return to Italy after her divorce.

She is a small woman of about forty-five, dark eyes behind eyeglasses, straight, black hair, dressed plainly and unassumingly. Unlike the cab driver, she shrugs when I tell her how warm it is in Livorno compared to Canada at this time of year. She tells me she speaks English but prefers we talk in Italian. She is not surprised in the least that I speak Italian and English, and although not exactly exuding warmth, is pleasant enough in her manner as she shows me how to make my own espresso in the morning, and says that I am welcome to enjoy the water and yogurt in the fridge, and that croissants will be delivered in the morning for breakfast unless I prefer bread to toast. "Here are two keys" that I should always carry with me, she says. The blue one is for my room and the red one is for entry into the building. "Of course, don't lose the keys. It will be very complicated but not impossible to replace them, at your cost."

The streets to the restaurant twist and turn "like a tedious argument / Of insidious intent / To lead you to an overwhelming question" to quote T.S. Eliot but are empty of fellow pedestrians, and silent.

There are few cars on Via Giotto. I don't really have a question or any questions at this point. Only one light shines in the homes I pass, and when I look up, many of the windows in the apartment blocks are dark. The silence and lack of people and cars makes me wonder, indeed, of "insidious intent" on the street. This is especially true at the edge of the park, Villa Regina. There are four teenagers sitting on a park bench under the statue of an important-looking Victorian, rolling tobacco and no doubt something a little stronger. I savour the irony for a moment. They barely look up as I pass. The path through the park is empty and full of dark shadows; a few streetlamps shine along the path but only a small patch of light dispels the gloom because of the thick overhang from the trees. On the other side of the park is the Hotel Boston, and not much seems to be going on there when I walk past.

I am amazed how silent the streets Borgo S. Jacopo and Borgo dei Cappuccini are compared to Viale Italia, a block over; Viale Italia buzzes with cars and buses, nonstop. And my only question, "Where is everybody?" is answered unexpectedly when at a bar/café on the corner I see three people laughing and seated at one of two tables that hug the café wall. A friend of theirs half-sits and half-leans forward on his heels off the edge of his motorcycle at the same time, and is telling the three of them something humorous. All four of them are young and smoking. The white light of the café falls in the shape of a square, half on the sidewalk and half on the street, and catches thin, blue-grey wisps of cigarette smoke above their table. It is a scene painted by Edward Hopper, but with Italian charm rather than American melancholy.

The restaurant I am searching for turns out to be just up the street from the laughing café table. To my surprise, I am early. I begin to read the posted outdoor menu when the waiter for the evening turns up behind my shoulder and tells me they do not open until eight.

I have about forty minutes to kill, so I cross the street to a stationery shop. After a brief but fastidious exchange with the owner, I buy a pack of ink cartridges for my Kaweco sport fountain pen for €1.20. The small shop is an odd mixture of paper stationery, kitschy gifts, souvenir coffee cups and glasses, notebooks, ink. The place needs a good dusting.

He is pleased to have at least one customer before he closes for dinner.

He is even more pleased when I ask if I can try to see if the ink cartridge works, and gives me an exaggerated and magnanimous "Ma si," and pulls out a slip of paper already full of scribbles.

He appears to be older than I am, but oddly adopts a deferential attitude. He lets me know he believes and understands I am a proper gentleman. I play along, self-conscious and half amused. Perhaps he hopes I will return soon for more ink. He is delighted when I produce the exact change.

The performance over, I walk to the corner for a view of the old harbour, and then into a café for an espresso before dinner. Here are gathered a small, young crowd between the ages of twenty and thirty. They are having beers, wine, orange- or red-coloured aperitifs in tall glasses with ice. They are dressed in the universal uniform of the young-—jeans and runners—but the jeans on the women are skin-tight and the sneakers on the men are fanciful, both in how they are laced and the silver and black colours. The sneakers look like they would appear normal on a moon walk. My presence here is irrelevant and, as older women often repeat about themselves, invisible.

The bourgeois approach or attitude—the one Modigliani railed against or tried to purge himself from in Paris—resurfaces in the restaurant. It is a mannered approach, governed by an overreliance on decorum in the way the waiter behaves with me, but in painting it is a focus on rules, on should and should not, on what is permissible and not permissible as art, instead of an artist's own way of seeing or doing. The external social world imposes itself on the internal world of the artist and what he can create.

This is not to say the waiter is not a decent, polite, and jolly guy. It is simply that Modigliani understood that everything in art is performance or artificial, and what he was trying to get to or capture in his paintings was his view of what was essential and real in a person, to capture what is beautiful as he understood it. His interest in spiritualism and drugs were an extension of his aesthetic. Both activities reach to extend beyond what is known, to be stimulated towards a deeper reality, a profounder truth hidden from view by everyday reality. "The sea makes a deep, inhuman sound," wrote the poet Wallace Stevens and, "She (the artist) sang beyond the genius of the sea."

The waiter is performing, and I am also: as a proper gentleman/writer, writing all this down while waiting for my dinner to arrive, glass of Orvieto white wine on my left.

Modigliani was a performer, often a showman. Picasso, always the patient observer, once shrewdly remarked, "You may find Utrillo drunk anywhere, but how is it Modi is always drunk at the corner of Boulevard du Montparnasse and Boulevard Raspail (Café La Rotonde) or Le Dome…"

Modigliani's love of a public or audience must have included traffic.

Modi, like many of the Paris avant-garde, loved to shock, to cross the bourgeois line wherever it was drawn. It was also part of his impish, iconoclastic nature. He was shy, well-mannered, but once under the influence of drugs or alcohol, aggressive and angry. The courtly prince and the scorned angry poet lived as Siamese twins attached to the same beating heart. The performance at some point took over his life.

The waiter's performance is impeccable tonight. His little nods of approval as I order, his careful and unobtrusive pouring of wine before and after dinner, his genial smile while clearing my plate, the courteous placing of my bill: all aim at being both gracious and natural. No tempestuous drama or passion. My own gestures and replies are also a performance. Unlike Modi or the waiter, my mask is a pen and notebook.

Paris, 1907, La Vie Boheme

Amedeo Modigliani:

I left rue Caulaincourt and for a time lived in the Hotel du Tertre right behind Sacre Coeur on Place du Tertre. I soon could not pay Bouscarat, the owner, and fretted how I was to escape my debt when, one evening, the plaster ceiling collapsed in my room. I am blessed, I thought. I naturally told him I was going to sue him for one hundred thousand francs. Told him I suffered damages both internal and external. Bouscarat, in a rage, threw me out and I was free of my debt.

I continued to work at 7 Place Jean-Baptiste Clement, several blocks over.

I live alone, and, apart from my zinc tub and mattress, own very little. It is easier for me to change addresses this way: when I am unable to pay my rent or evicted. I sometimes exit in such a hurry that I leave behind my work, or the landlord seizes my paintings. The rooms are all cold and damp and smell of mould. I used to be bourgeois.

The city is one great boiling cauldron of art. Everywhere I turn there is an artist and a movement: Impressionists (yesterday's movement), Cubists, Fauves, Futurists, Expressionists. Renoir, Utrillo, Dufy, Matisse, Picasso, Bucci, Vlaminck, Derain. I love Cézanne's work. I look at his work to learn to see with new eyes.

My walls are covered with canvases and my portfolios are full of drawings. Yet, I feel everything I do is incomplete, uncertain, not really saying what I want to say in every line and colour. I can see a fault in each and every one of the paintings I have done. I hesitate. Venice and Livorno did not prepare me.

Louis Latourette, the poet and journalist, paid me a visit the other day and I told him, "My Italian eyes cannot get used to the light of Paris…such an all-embracing light. I am like Cellini when he first came to France and said the air is clearer than misty Italy. You cannot imagine what new themes I have thought up, in violet, deep orange, and ochre... There is no way of making them (the paintings) sing now. I lack the right technique."

I destroyed everything a few days later; only a few drawings and a woman's head remain. Childish baubles done when I was a dirty bourgeois. I must return to sculpture soon.

On my evenings out, I now wear a corduroy jacket, red scarf, broad-brimmed hat, and quarrel with Bucci in the Café Vachette over who is the best painter alive in Italy. It is obvious: my best friend Oscar Ghiglia. In France it is Matisse and Picasso. I almost told him, "And me," but shy, I held back. Bucci now avoids me.

I have decided to paint the cherry tree directly in front of my window on rue Lepic. I love the delicate white and light-pink coloured flowers, the small, vivid green leaves, the weathered grey tree trunk, arms raised as if in supplication and celebration to spring

Cool weather, grey skies, and I have my first admirer and patron, Dr. Paul Alexandre. He is a tall, handsome man with delicate manners, and is kindly disposed towards artists. Although not rich, he has purchased my painting, *The Jewess*, for a few hundred francs— but it is his faith and deep admiration for me for which I am most grateful.

It is a painting of my wealthy mistress, Maude Abrantes. She is elegant and wild-haired, but left—pregnant—for America, never to be heard from again. My child?

Dr. Alexandre had encouraged me to enter the Salon des Indépendants in the spring of 1908. I showed five works: *The Jewess*, two nudes, a study for *The Idol*, and a drawing. Sold nothing.

Dr. Alexandre and his brother Jean have organized a phalanstery of artists, a kind of lay monastery, after the socialist thinker, Fourier, at 7 rue de Delta near the Gare du Nord. I live there on and off. It is a barn-like building with a vast hall, a few cubicles, and a shabby garden nearby. Paul and his brother have evicted the washerwomen who had set up their business there to make room for the artists.

I have made friends here with the painter, Doucet, and the sculptor, Maurice Drouard. Drouard's face is dark and brooding; his eyes under black brows pierce inward and his hair is like a waving, thick black flame. A dramatic face…naturally, I painted his portrait.

Doucet and I climb the fence around the Metro station, Barbès-Rochechouart, and steal the wood used to build the new line. Working in stone continues to be hard on my poor lungs, but I still feel sculpture is my true destiny. I hope wood will not make me so ill, as does stone.

I quarrel with both almost every day.

Before Christmas 1908, I smashed some of Drouard's sculptures and Doucet's paintings, and ripped up some of my own immature drawings. All that survived were the twenty or so paintings and drawings Dr. Alexandre bought before my absinthe rage. He is astonished at my behaviour, but still tells his family I am "a well brought up young man." Drouard and Doucet are outraged. They loathe me and I loathe them, and do not ask for their forgiveness.

They do not understand destruction is sometimes necessary before the new can emerge. My soul is pure.

Dr. Alexandre supplies me with hashish and believes, when taken in moderation, it can stimulate and enhance an artist's art. Both ether and absinthe are available for three sous. More than once, now, the good doctor has tried to steer me towards moderation. If I do not mix my hashish pellets with wine, ether, or absinthe, I enjoy how it makes me last longer, both as the pursuer and the pursued; how my gentle, deep strokes and her moans form and hold paradise for a moment. The insatiable, fiery mouth of her vulva never truly says 'that's enough.'

New Year's Eve party, 1908

Andre Warnod, ex-sketcher and writer:
Modigliani stands in the hallway of my atelier.
Offering each new arrival a green bullet of hashish
'You will be a true vivid god tonight,
Janus arrives this evening, welcome him
Enjoy this ancient lotus flower he says,
Smiles his beautiful smile and pops again
One into his red, laughing mouth.
We dance, laugh, sing, fondle, and drink.
Later Modigliani stands by my punch bowl
Pours kerosene, poof...
'Viola, punch flambé,' he shouts.
The room is full of cigarette smoke, laughter, and dance
Streamers above the punch bowl catch fire
Flames run up the wall, sear wooden beams.
My guests frantic, scream, run
Modigliani continues to dance in front of the flaming bowl
Recites Nietzsche and D'Annunzio to no one in particular
Well, at least he did not dance naked.

Cité Falguière studio, spring, 1909

Paul Alexandre:
I tell him I have sold nothing, to stop drugs and drink.
Burdened by debts, rent, restaurant bills,
He sometimes stays in bed all day
Too poor to heat his room or leave.
Weak body and worn-down nerves
Unknown mistresses
Buy drink, a little food, paints
Studio floor is covered in white insecticide powder
To protect him from fleas
Columns of bedbugs, stray rats.
When he sleeps or can paint
Makes a few francs drawing in the cafés
Tourists thrilled to meet an authentic shabby artist
Half-drunk, unshaven, eyes dirty little pools of black light.
Fashionable galleries, art dealers
All ignore him, but a few fellow artists
And the half-blind lawyer's clerk Pere Angely.
'I've only got one buyer and he's blind,' Modi tells me.

Livorno, Summer 1909

Eugénia Modigliani:
He arrived home exhausted before his twenty-fifth birthday
The air warm and luxurious, sky dark Egyptian blue
I asked about Paris.
In the beginning he read at the Bibliothèque Sainte-Geneviève
Visited museums, galleries, latest exhibitions
At the Académie Colarossi sketched nude models,
Mostly Italian immigrants, until the light failed.
In the evenings found laughter, quarrels, at the Café Rotonde
Picasso, Georges Braque, Juan Gris, strong coffee
Song at the Lapin Agile
Cheap dinners at Chez Rosalie on rue Campagne-Première:

"Italian flows between us like sweet honey, Mama. Rosalie prepares
Italian dishes with extra garlic, special just for me. She loves me. I
pay her with drawings. She uses the paper to wrap food; sometimes
rats in the basement eat the piled-up extra drawings. I do not fault
her," he says.

Short, dry, ironic Garsin smile
Cannot remove stains on his pants and overcoat
Heels worn down, like him
Eyes tired, complacent, dark half-moons
Roman face now a beautiful ruin,
Curved sad mouth wears an absinthe stink
I dare not ask about women,
My fear of venereal disease, hopes and dreams
Cause of his transformation.
It is enough here in the carriage home
My love destroying me.

Livorno, August 1909

Amedeo Modigliani:
Part of my restoration includes writing philosophy pamphlets
In the morning after breakfast with my brilliant Aunt Laure
Read the 'barbarian hammer' Nietzsche
Introspection turned into philosophy
In the garden on sunny afternoons
When the tide is low, inhale marine scent on the breeze
Drink Livorno punch, half coffee and half rum boiled together
Eat Mama's strong fish soup, nap after lunch
Gossip at the dinner table about my Parisian friends:
Did you know Severini and I met one evening on rue Lepic
We recognized each other immediately
By the way we dressed as Tuscans.
Picasso's French, a Spanish painter, is terrible.
Poet critic Max Jacob believes drugs heighten poetic imagination
Help you predict the future, I do no tell Mama this,
André Salmon is a poet, man of letters and a friend
Aunt Laure shudders at the mention of poets
Mama nods her head up and down
Watches me talk, says nothing
Giovanni Papini sends letters about Schopenhauer
My sister Margherita smokes too much
I stare at the same moon every night
In the western sky that shines over Paris
Sometimes visit the Caffe Bardi
Where is Romiti? Natali? my old painter friends?
Ugo Bardi finds some absinthe
We toast to health and friendship
My moods are like angry newspaper sheets

Or I feel like old sad leaves lying on the grass one moment
Violent sudden sea waves the next, *una pazzia.*
I must be patient, gather my strength
Like the moon every night, grow beauty
Before I can return to Paris. Sculpt light. Shine.

Part Four: The Rain, Anna Akhmatova,
and Beatrice Hastings nude

October 1909, Brâncuşi studio, 54 rue du Montparnasse… or a short history of Modi's career as a sculptor.

The new Modi is actually the old Modi
Returned to Paris in sartorial splendour
Loose grey shirt, broad silk knotted scarf
Dark leather boots and pants
One bent leg on the bench leans forward
In the photo he looks defiant and posed, cigarette in left hand,
Other hand is on his right hip, eyes wounded and vague
Affair with Elvira new
The vogue in Montmartre: cocaine, ether, lesbianism and Cubism

2

Between 1909 and 1912, Modi and Brancusi work together
Reject Rodin's method of first constructing the work
Using clay shaped over and over again
On an armature, then a plaster cast, next a metal mold
Filled with red hot bronze and left to cool.
Brancusi tells Modi: 'What good is the practice of modeling?
It leads to sculptured cadavers.'
Only what has been cut from stone beginning to end is true sculpture
Stone waits for the sculptor to release image already there
The same way paper waits for the poem
Both emerge from the will to shape desire
Create and organize surprise with each cut, each word.

3

Modi moves between Montmartre and Montparnasse
Between painting and sculpture

Between two groups of artists who often hate each other
Steals wood and stone from Metro construction sites.
We sometimes carve together
From my chisel, a face emerges round as a pear
Curved stone refined like a scalloped shell

I reach for the purity of infinity
Modi mysterious posed masks
Nose cut sharp as a knife, slanted olive-eyes
Pressed small thin lips, chorographic hair like tiny rivers
Compressed serene sorrow surges into and out of stone

4

Augustus John, the Welsh painter, visits Modigliani's studio in Montmartre
Buys two sculptures: "For some days afterwards I found myself
Under the hallucination of meeting people in the street who might
Have posed for them… Can Modi have discovered a new secret aspect of reality?"

5

Meanwhile near Place Saint-Michel, the cut poem:
In a station of the Metro
The apparition of these faces in the crowd;
Petals on a wet, black bough
— Ezra Pound

6

Nina Hamnett, artist, writer, bisexual Queen of Bohemia (Paris)
Visits Modigliani's messy and dirty studio on rue St. Gothard
Admires full figured sensual caryatid drawings on the wall
For an unfinished 'temple of pleasure,'
Carved heads, 'pillars of tenderness,' are under the window
Near the end of the bed is a large spiderweb and a large black spider
He has grown attached to it
Calls the spider his only painting companion

Does not wish to disturb her web.
Flattered, Nina can ignore poverty
But the spider makes her nervous and refuses him
Nina, then dance naked for me again, he says
The way you do at the Café Rotonde
Let me delight in your slender legs and body
Large teardrop tits, neatly trimmed and scented red pubic hair.

Livorno Diary #5: Casa Modigliani Sings the Nudes

The next day begins with the loud opening and closing of the door at six a.m. at my B&B. I hear a box drop with a thud, followed by the opening/closing of the fridge door, water running from the tap, rustling of paper, and an impatient sharp porcelain click of plate against plate. I lie in bed waiting for the B&B owner's son to leave for what I assume is a delivery of croissants.

It is a bright, sunny morning when I head out, route marked out once again on my iPhone. To my astonishment, I find Modigliani's first home, without first wandering around in circles for hours along grey paving-stone streets with endless small clothing shops, shoe stores, cafès, pastry and bread shops, butcher shops, fish vendors, and restaurants. Instead, I arrive without peregrinations at 38 Via Roma, Casa Modigliani. Next door on the glass shop-door is a poster-sized, seated, orange-coloured nude, "Modigliani" scrawled across the top covering her ample breasts. Inside, *Il Cioccolatino Modigliani,* The Little Chocolate Modigliani shop, sells miniature chocolate heads of Modigliani's sculptured faces that are flavored with absinthe, called *Sogno di Dedo*, Dedo's Dream, along with the usual chocolate fare.

He would have smiled at the irony and then raged, after a drink, at being exploited so shamelessly.

I cannot figure out which sculpture the chocolates are based on, but the primitive African mask influence is there on the small oval pieces. No Brâncuși.

The Casa is not far from the Piazza Attias, a busy corner where there is a large, realistic bronze head of Modigliani looking much like what I have seen of him in photos: handsome, Marcello Mastroianni look-a-like face; thick hair brushed to the left across a wide brow; well-shaped, almost feminine cheekbones; sensual lower lip; penetrating eyes; shirt open at the neck, giving him a look of casual disarray. The whole sculpture is posed and serious, like many of the portraits he did of others. It is a boy/man face—the kind of face most women find appealing.

There is a plaque beside the window on the second floor of the Casa announcing this is the birthplace of Amedeo Modigliani, painter, (but not "and sculptor"), put up by the city in 1959 on his birthday, July 12. He would have been seventy-five. The walls outside of the house (actually, the entire block) look like they have been restored or re-stuccoed in recent years, compared to a photo taken shortly after the plaque went up.

The wall has a smooth finish and is not pitted with crumbling plaster; the shutters painted a fresh Italian green.

I press the buzzer and a woman's voice asks who is it and that right now she is busy with two clients. I tell her I am here to see the Casa Modigliani and promise not to disturb her and her guests. I am let in and walk up two short flights of grey concrete stairs, pause to consider if these are the same stairs the young Modigliani walked on, and arrive at a red varnish-stained door.

There are four rooms. The hallways and two large rooms on each end are filled with copies of family, childhood, and personal photos, as well as prints of most but not all of Modigliani's paintings and sculptures scattered around the globe to different art museums such as the Tate Modern, The Guggenheim, National Gallery of Washington, George Pompidou Centre in Paris, and the National Art Gallery of Modena. There is nothing of his original work here. Even the letters he wrote to his family, friends, school report cards, and the photos of his time in Paris are copies. There is no mention where the original letters and photos are archived, or if part of some other collection. There are also a few articles preserved under glass, announcing an event feting Livorno's famous painter; a newspaper interview with Lunia Czechowska one of Modigliani's last models and important family friend after his marriage, and the mistress of his last art dealer, Léopold Zborovski.

One of the rooms includes a heavy, dark wooden desk. Behind it, and half full, is a collection, some donated by the authors, of books discussing Modigliani's work, in French, English, Spanish, Romanian, Russian, and of course Italian. What is most interesting, however, is a series of paintings done by contemporary artists riffing off Modigliani's nudes at the back of the apartment. The contemporary artists mimic the erotic languor of his paintings, but one in particular references Modigliani's less famous *Nude with a Necklace*. In both paintings the hands are underneath the head, arms spread across the back of a cushion, and both paintings are eyeless. But, Modigliani's painting (as do almost all his nudes), exudes a quiet sizzle or erotic aura, and is a generous celebration of the female body whereas the contemporary rendition is clearly ironic or a parody of Modigliani's female nude.

Félix Vallotton, a contemporary French printmaker and painter of Modigliani remarked that a successful nude painting or drawing "must have in it… a dram of concupiscence."

Modigliani's nudes fill the frame, and as art critics have noted, echo classical Greek and Roman sculpture, Modi's first love.

But what makes the nudes fresh, and were startling to an early 20th century audience, is how they depict and combine celebration and directness. The nudes are uninhibited, and some have suggested post-coitus or even pre-arousal. The nude women are plainly themselves, unadorned and solitary. There is no background to distract or puzzle the viewer, except a cushion or a fully coloured divan, and no reference to any classical myth or location to gussy it up or make legitimate the viewer seeing a nude woman's body in all its uninhibited, curved, voluptuous beauty. There is only one nude that is not sensual: *Female Nude with a Hat;* the neck is drawn on a sharp angle instead of smooth and round, and the eyes look back at the viewer with smoldering anger, mouth twisted.

Modigliani's nudes want to take us back to the original garden— unlock the gates, climb up and put the apple back on the tree.

There is, in fact, a garden at the back of the apartment. Next door is a growling dog who does not like me standing on the balcony looking at the thick, bushy rows of cherry tomatoes and his peach tree. I wonder if he is the ancestor of the dog Modigliani's mother complained about. Next door, some of the neighbour's laundry hangs out to dry in the sun, and directly under my nose is a withered potted plant used by someone as an ashtray, a few cigarette butts crushed into the dirt and looking like something dead.

38 Via Rome is where the famous debtor scene took place, but the actual bedroom is a floor above, rented and unavailable. It is from this address that the family moved to smaller rooms on Piazza Magenta after the collapse of the mining and lumber stocks in Sardinia. Somewhere on Piazza Magenta, renamed Piazza della Victoria (there is no city hall plaque), is where Modigliani returned home from Paris, exhausted, in 1909, and stayed three months—long enough for his strength to return—before hastily returning to the art scene in Paris. Directly in front of the Piazza is the church Santa Maria del Soccorso, built in 1835. It is surrounded by a park, and when I visited in the fall, dry leaves scratched, tapped, and when the breeze picked up, raced across the sidewalk as I made my way to the final residence of the Modigliani family on Via Leonardo Cambini where there is a plaque to Emmanuel Modigliani, Amedeo's socialist brother.

Is this the park where Aunt Laure sometimes felt she would be raped in the middle of the afternoon as she walked back home after a short walk after lunch?

On the park benches and gravel paths there is not a single poet in sight under what seems like an impossibly crisp blue-on-blue autumn sky.

Unable to sculpt anymore due to the effect of dust on his weak lungs, the problem of finding a ground-floor studio, and unable to sell his sculptures, he gave up sculpting.

Modigliani was ignored and gradually evolved into a penniless and disorderly, dark romantic painter; a drug- and alcohol-addicted (hashish and absinthe), mad, chaotic lover of poor women (often his models), damned women, (dance hall dancers or circus performers), and talented women (Anna Akhmatova, Russian poet; Beatrice Hastings, writer, are two examples), and near the last years of his life suffered from TB. He painted clear, classically shaped and influenced nudes, and psychologically expressive portraits. Modigliani was not interested in fragmenting reality, analytical dissection of its parts, or in trying to capture the sequential steps of motion (Cubism and Synthetic Cubism). His nudes are about round desire, curved sensuality, and the uninhibited languor of pleasure.

By contrast, his friend and rival, Picasso, is sober, calculating, and cautious as a small pawnshop owner, cruel and dominant in his relationships with women. Picasso is one of the founders of Cubism: his paintings distort and reshape the female nude, his portraits become unrecognizable, and face and/or body parts are fragmented and rearranged into what look like geometric angles. He structures his anger on a flat canvas. His talent is protean, considered groundbreaking, and is embraced by the wealthy art world.

Modigliani's life as a painter is one long stumble. His life sputters; his art is barely recognized. It is in his nudes where Modi finds some kind of control, where he expresses his unbearable need to connect with a woman's body and soul.

Picasso is the opposite. Picasso releases his anger onto his Cubist nudes, connection be damned.

38 Via Leonardo Cambini (same number as Via Roma) is the location of the last Modigliani family residence and one block away from the edge of the park. It is here that Modi returned in 1912, more physically wrecked than his first return in 1909.

His brother and mother found him a flat with a garden and a studio, and asked him to remain in Livorno. For his health, for his mother, *per il amore di Dio* (for the love of God), they both told him. He refused and returned to Paris near the end of 1912.

The light and natural beauty of the Mediterranean poured, as it does this afternoon, into him one last time.

Before

Before dreams of trees, unfinished sculptures
Hashish, late night Calvados
Before eyeless detached long-necked portraits
Or a thin torn gauze dress in morning light
Before the colour of sunset on a reclining nude
Or bee-stung nipples, black hair, round hips
Before paint caressed onto a blank canvas
Or exhaustion and spring serein rain
Before Paris was an aroused nude
Pleurisy, or the old red-bricked harbor of Livorno
Before green-blue sea deliriums and fever
Or eyeless masked faces in dreams
Before abandoned and found lovers
Or rose, blood-stained handkerchiefs
Before rage, drunkenness, and poetry
Or the unachievable purity of a pure artist
There is simply a boy adored by his mother.

Paris, April 1910 & May 1911

Anna Akhmatova:
After three years of pursuit, declarations of love
I married a famous poet, literary critic, traveler.
I do not know whether or not I love Nikolay Gumilyov
It seems it is my fate to be his wife.
We are here on our honeymoon
He gives lectures, attends meetings
I sit in the same café every day and drink my morning coffee
Dryly read the newspaper, write in my journal.

2
Modigliani's beautiful classical French fell on me
Like an unexpected shadow from a Baudelaire poem
I cannot forget his voice, in his eyes a golden gleam
Accompanied by exquisite manners.
No friend, no past lover, never mundane things
Only a quiet ring of solitude and a love of sculpture
'He was that rarity, a painter who knew and loved poetry.'
Recited, by the hour, Laforge, Mallarmé, Lautréamont.

3
A year later waits for me in the Salon des Indépendants
He does not approach when I finally appear
Instead we visit the Egyptian department at the Louvre
He dreams only of Egypt, 'the rest is of no importance.'
Rejects Cubism, anything fashionable,
Makes little money, winter in Paris is harsh
He is thinner, eyes sunk deeper
Proud aristocrat heart and soul

How does he survive?
Still handsome next to the Venus di Milo, he says:
'Women of beauty worthy of painting or sculpting
seem heavily dressed in their clothes.'

4

Firm right hand moves forward and back again like a wave
He draws a quick thin charcoal line
Then an unexpected curve
Slanted eyeless head rests on my slender shoulder
Arm on an angle
Singular small round tit captured
So is the gentle bump of my stomach
I emerge a sleeping nude Venus on cushions
Fresh from the blank white sea.
He squints to study each line, lips pressed, concentrating
Satisfied he kisses my toes
Considers the inside of my knee
I let him travel up the length of my thigh
Inhale my scent
Pauses to ask about the little prisoner
Trapped at the top of my moist hill
I blush pink, red, and white like a cherry blossom.
Slow sly shy grin emerges
He says my face shows divine progress.

5

On a bench in the Jardin du Luxembourg
We recited Verlaine under his old black umbrella
Delighted we remembered the same verses
Soft tap of summer rain kept the beat
At night it was his footsteps under my window.

6

His door locked
I toss a surprise bouquet of roses

One by one through an open window
He returned to find a formed charmed pattern
Convinced I somehow entered.

7

You say I ignite you
Through poems
Your gypsy soul flares
I am your female *Cesare:*
I found, I saw, I know
Your sad-eyed mystery opens and closes
Shadow on the *claire de lune* streets of the Latin Quartier.

8

Our destiny began when I did not return to Paris
Melancholy and poems followed
Both were there already under our skin, our eyes
Tarnish already there inside the dream, on the silver streets
Never in my heart.

Winter in Paris, 1911-1912, Amedeo Modiglani:

My cough always begins with cold weather
Light at the beginning of day
Like the pale yellow bruise on my chest.
My lungs are a pair of complaining songbirds.
Grey bare trees, sky not much better
Wishing it was summer
The origins of my art an inarticulate purity?
Loathe money economy
Love Ancient Egyptian sculpture, African masks.
I refuse to lead or follow Picasso & friends.
Art is a history of false revolutions
Broken words on some critic's pages.
Truth is just another mask
Flesh and light my true addictions
I must learn again and again.
Is there an Eastern European woman
Somewhere who can save me?

Winter Dream, 1913

I am told my paintings and sculpture do not sell
My mother suggests I come home for lunch
But I live in Paris I reply
I feel humiliated
Told not to worry, something will sell next day.
I have no money nor anyone to dine with in the city
To kill time, I wander into a hotel lobby
See a small diaphanous snake under a chair
It is an ancient symbol from the future
I have a gnawing feeling it no longer matters
World, people, city, artists
Continue in their small gestures
It all amounts to nothing
How to continue
How to paint futility.

1913

Gaby, Modi's Model:
We met a few nights ago
He was unshaven and gone
Courting his green mistress
I did not notice him at the back of the Rotonde
Windowless and dark like his eyes.
He was to my surprise short
Large black hat pulled carelessly to one side
Holding down thick black hair
He stood in a stained painter's jacket
Brown corduroy pants
Scarlet neck scarf with a jaunty knot
He quoted a sing-song Italian poem
'Passa la rondine e con essa estate.
E anch'io mi dico passero.'

Sweet mutterings of birds at dusk in summer
All pass away into the tomb of eternity.
He repeated in beautiful French
But his eyes, oh, his cold dark eyes
They moved over the top
Of my half-moon curves like a pair of hands
Caressed my unattractive large hips
Held my neck and lips.

He reached across the table to touch my hair
White dust covered the back of his hand
Fingers long like a pianist
He saw me look, smiled and said:

'I am also a sculptor; touch guides my chisel.'
I instinctively pulled away from his reach
Even though I admit he is handsome.
He told me he found himself early as an artist
I, on the other hand, found myself an artist's model and lover.

I arrived next day and after a brief hello he asked me to undress
Lover or not, five francs I insisted
He offered immortality which is never edible.
The light was weak so he opened the front windows
Swept his hand out towards distant blue boulevard rooftops
Eternal grey Paris sky.

Your breasts are fit to suckle men to create a new Rome
Perfect round Madonna face before she sinned
Sit here on the divan, get comfortable but do not look at me
I should have told you to trim your hairy middle
Please do not complain of the cold, close your eyes
I suffer for my art unlike that fraud Picasso.

Caryatid, 1913

He paid me with a small blue sketch
Face like an African mask, heavy oval head
Slanted eyes and brows
Full round breasts, thick curved bent legs
Caryatid for the temple of pleasure
An unfinished temple, he said, like you.

Paris, 1914

Elvira, La Quique, Standing Nude
Modigliani feels his blood surge towards her:
Her beautiful shape always creates a gasp in his mind.
He translates and draws her narrow
From shoulders to her waist
One quick turn of the wrist, the line
Flares and is now a curved sensual hip.
He begins to fill in the white folded shirt
Just above the plateau
There where they all want to place kisses
Paint glows an orange fall afternoon light
Round, small, and firm uneven breasts parted
Tit on the left slightly lower
Almond-shaped eyes without orbs, mouth set,
Pretty oval Venus face from the Mediterranean's shore
Her posture hieratic simplicity
He has painted her naked from the waist up
As if a tambourine player at ease, Tarantella dance over.
They met in a café near Place Pigalle
Case of *coup de foudre*, lightning flash found love
Fast and furious at 7 Place Jean-Baptiste Clement
Or is it in the little garden next to rue Ravignan
There they danced naked for anyone
Under the gas lights three hashish days later.
La Quique's firm breasts wagged, forefingers formed
Devil's horns on a bull's head, she charged him
Ole shouted the matador, his finger
A picador's lance entered her from behind
Laughter loud as a church bell

At each pass under his raised arm
According to Mme Gabrielle, the next-door neighbour,
She called next morning; Elvira's portrait hung on the wall

2

Daughter of a Marseillaise prostitute, Spanish father,
Runs away to Paris at the age of fifteen, then abroad with one
After another until kept in Berlin by a Dutch Baron.
Learns German, to sing, returns to Paris
One of the many orphans Montmartre collected
Cocaine ruined Elvira's voice.
1914 arrested with a troupe near the front lines speaking German.
Disbelieved, she was shot as a spy.

Elvira, singer and model:
    She waits in a small café not far from his studio. She knows he paints until the late afternoon, takes small sips from a short-stemmed demitasse rimmed with a thin gold band after each brush stroke. She remembers how it caught the light whenever he raised it to his lips. How he looked at her. Paused. Looked again, to be certain. They both sat in front of the open window. It was a May morning, sunlight white as silver. Drunk, covered in sweat when he finally smiled and put his brushes down.
    She remembers the lovemaking was never the same. Sometimes gentle, the air around them breaking into murmurs. Arms and legs wrapped around each other in the shape of a half-formed cocoon. Or he poured into her, gripped her breasts like a drowning man. Mounted. Pushed into her in a furious rage, ending in delirium.
    She knows he is now preparing his bath. Session over. Recognizes the Italian woman who just left his studio: Picasso's former lover and model. She walks past in a blue skirt, white shirt puffed at the shoulders. Wide, white hat with a blue band. Face tired, languorous.
    She wants to see him before the theatrical troupe she joined goes to the Front. Perform before the cold winter rains arrive. The war began in August. It was supposed to be over already. The hot summer weather continues into the fall.
    Today, it is a hot day at the end of September. The heat lingers in the stairwell. She can feel it as she climbs the two flights of stairs to his studio. Her armpits are damp. Her soft middle, damp and moist with anticipation and desire. She does not know why. It is natural for her to leave all her lovers.
    She knocks. Turns the long door-handle. Enters the room. The first thing she sees is his small, white back. It leans against the curved end of the grey zinc tub. She shuts the door behind her gently. Turns the small lock and imagines for a brief moment both his fingers knot-

ted on her nipple.

They stare at each other like uncertain chess players. She takes in the odours of the room: sardines, tobacco smoke, mould, decayed wood, scented orange soap, varnish, oil paint. He turns away. Continues to bath.

She watches him pour water over his head. Lather his hair, eyes closed. It is then she approaches him. Takes the cup from this hand. Pours the lukewarm water over his head. Pours again. Asks him to stand. He rises up like a young Poseidon, dripping.

She pours water down his back. Scrubs with her palms. They both laugh softly. This is how he finally greets her. She scrubs the muscles on the backs of his legs. Asks him to turn and raise his arms above his head. Takes the cloth and runs it down from his armpit to his thigh as if she is drawing him. Then the other side. Soaps his stomach, pubic hair. Pours water. Watches it run through the small trough on each side of his cock. Soaps his testicles. Moves her hand back and forth over the head. It stirs in her hand like a small, delicate sea creature. She smiles. Leans forward and kisses the tip. Looks up to see what effect this has on him. He draws a thin, soapy moustache on her smiling upper lip. Finished, she steps back and waits for him.

He steps out of the tub towards her. Kisses her forehead. Nose. Ears. Moves his tongue across her lips. She grips his tongue with her lips. They lean into each other. He unfastens her buttons. She now holds her hands above her head. Her breasts spill out in one quick liberated movement, hungry to be themselves.

They fall in one embrace on the bed. The sunlight in the room is still.

Canvas untouched.

**It has never been established with any certainty if Modigliani started or finished painting Elvira in 1914, before she was shot, or if in fact he painted her in 1918, entirely from memory, as a kind of memorial after learning of her death.

June days, 1914

Beatrice Hastings' Journal:

I left for Paris to escape that penny-pinching ex-schoolmaster A.R. Orage, my so-called co-editor at *The New Age*. There was also the problem of his wife. Aphrodite must have howled at our affair. Our mutual belief in theosophy was no help at all.

I was the one who first published Ezra Pound and Katherine Mansfield; now look where they are! Pound invited here, there, and everywhere in London; Katherine married to that idiot John Middleton Murray and living in Menton, France.

I begged, tried, and I cried for her to say no, but she still married him. Orage's secret declarations of love made matters worse. Prayed to Sappho. I shudder to think Murray now places his lips where I used to, opens her small apricot to his touch.

I spoke French and longed to escape the wreckage that was becoming my life. Heard about *les suffragettes* and their outrageousness. They cut their hair short. Wore trousers. Paris was the logical destination.

I arrived in May 1914 as the Paris correspondent of *The New Age*.

I fancy artists and the bohemian life, and when all is said and done, I am a writer. A free woman for and of the new age. Taking and finding my pleasure as I please. Logical.

I began writing a weekly column called "Impressions of Paris" under the *nom de plume* Alice Mornings. Pun on "mourning," ha.

It took little effort to find the Spanish painter everyone was talking about called Picasso. Went over to find him at the Bateau-Lavoir over in Montmartre, a former piano factory, locksmith's workshop, and now a squalid artist's quarters. The place oozes moisture. There is an unhealthy smell of mildew, cat piss, drains, and there is only one toilet on the ground floor—a hole really—with no latch on the door.

The rent is still cheap, fifteen francs a month. I am told Picasso has a patron and no longer lives here.

I found some of his work, nevertheless. He has moved the line in painting towards a kind of geometry. *Les Demoiselles d'Avignon* is both ugly and angry. Strange, startling angles. *Seated Nude* is all squares and cubes and oddly serene, severe, but I would not call it pretty. There is no love.

There is a new beauty in the air but many ask if the Cubists have left their senses.

I tell you all this by way of explaining my new handsome lover, the artist Amedeo Modigliani's *comportement*. He speaks lovely French. Classical. A pale and ravishing villain. And let us just say there is a little bad, a whiff of sad, and a dollop of mad about him. A modern- day Lord Byron minus the club foot. Both a pig and a pearl, ha.

But, he is clean. Bathes every day. He is thirty (claims he is twenty-seven) and I am thirty-five. You see…a true rogue.

He is called the Prince of Montparnasse, or "Modi" among his arty friends: Utrillo, Kisling, Soutine, Brâncuşi, one-armed Cendrars, fatso Rivera.

He dismisses the Cubists as unfeeling tricksters, the whole lot of them. Refuses to have their names, their art, talked about in his presence. This is especially true if he is drunk. Violent. Shouts and grabs and throws whatever is in reach: glass, soup spoon, coffee cup, plates; smashes café chairs. Pounds the table in outrage, demanding drink, lord of the café. I tell him to calm yourself, mention he is the son of a distinguished family. He screams he is an artist with a soul; they are all soulless. He is all storm, full of thunder and fury. Unbearable. I hold his arm and quickly whisper in his ear, "Let us go to my flat on 13 rue Norvins in Montmartre." Promise him a few green hashish pellets. Smile. Touch the inside of his trouser leg. Lower my eyelids.

His body is a slender mad tree in the wind with a head of curls. The hashish increases our appetite; my body bends towards him in need and ache. His motion is like one of Cleland's famous vermillion pistons. He pours his anger and love into me, and I am glad for it. His tongue feels raw like a cat's. Hold him close and we both shudder.

He falls asleep. The storm over. Later in his sleep I hear him mumble "Akhmatova." Sounds foreign. Russian?

The next day I repent. Write in my column about the evil effects of hashish, the fatal La Vie Boheme.

A.M meets B.H., 1914

We met at Chez Rosalie
Managed to raise my hat
Above my drunk and drugged head
Admired her *belle visage* and sat
Down to a plate before she could disapprove.
I returned the next day, bathed and shaved
Noted her cool black eyes
Hair cut short, modern
Modest jaw sloped on an angle
Like a cliff away from me.
I waited, waited to hear the Ligurian sea fall
Between her crevice, splash against her hips.
She pushed my hand away
Her breasts heaved and sighed like waves
Under her tight dress
Nipples outlined firm as a small knot
Thin grey socks followed curved muscle
Blue wool shawl on her shoulders.
She told me artists are folly, smiled.
The clatter of hooves on an empty street
Sunlight and smoke at Gare Montparnasse
Why did I not paint that, she asked?
And knew immediately she was attracted to me.
I wanted her curves on my hands
Lead a new rebellion against her past.
Come to my studio, you are the perfect caryatid
We are many artists and poets all
The place is called le Bateau-Lavoir
The way it creaks and storms on rainy days.

She did not explain why she cut her hair
I tell her Beatrice was Dante's *amante*
We can make *La Vita Nuova* our own:
Beautiful sinners, manifest beatitude.

Paris, May–June 1914

The poet and the artist, 13 rue Norvins, Montmartre:
Morning. Sunlight streams into the apartment. He stretches like a black cat. After living in ugly, oppressive poverty for eight harsh years he now finds himself in comfortable surroundings. Cut flowers in a vase. Furniture. A big china stove for cooking and heat. The pretty English cunt and I—no, not cunt, too harsh, he thinks, and smiles although it is lovely. The bitch and I live together in grand style: four rooms and a kitchen, a big hall, cabinet and conservatory. The rooms open onto a garden—*che bella aria*—a welcome respite after the foul air at le Bateau-Lavoir. The furniture is second-hand, but he does not care.

He thinks of her as his petite cherie. He admires her spirit, *la mia Bea*, my Bea. Reads Dante to her after their morning lovemaking. He tells her he adores her pretty breasts, her black hair, and asks her to grow it long again so he can paint it. She is small, but her sexual appetite is large. He complains to the Cubist painter, Jacques Lipchitz, that she likes to surprise him and bite his balls.

He repeats more than once to him her past love affairs are *complique*.

They go everywhere and do everything together. Late nights of drinking, hashish, films, work, cheap meals; tour Paris by night. She pays for everything. Money from Italy stopped because of the war.

He insists on showing her the "real" Paris. He explains, "You have only seen Paris, but I will show you *Pareeee.*"

He can see she adores him by the way she looks at him. He reminds her not to fall in love with him. The next day he changes his mind; "Yes, perhaps love will do both of us good," he tells her. He can tell she does not care what he says. She wants to care for him, be with him. The handsome rebel artist. "If this is love, so be it," he says to her. He needs her more than he is willing to admit. He is painting more now, almost a painting a week. He no longer attempts sculpture. She is the missing anchor since he arrived in Paris eight years ago.

In early July she needs to return to London to wrap up a few loose ends. He insists on accompanying her to the Gare du Nord. She ignores his demand until he stands in front of her taxi on Boulevard Montparnasse and begs her to let him into the cab. They arrive at the station and he faints against one of the carriages. Her fellow English travellers stare at her, and then at him, in astonishment and horror. She scolds him to stop his buffoonery. Making a spectacle. Reminds him of his work. Softens. "I promise you, I will return," she tells him.

"Madame, don't leave me," he shouts in a hoarse, pathetic voice as she boards the train. She tells him that someone told her he has been fiddling with one stone head after another for the past three years and "You'll be another three on a new design."

He replies, "Cretin," and glares at her. "Ma petite, he is right. I might have grown some asparagus in that time."

The entire scene is operatic. She now stands inside the carriage by the window, waving slowly her last goodbye. He is on the platform, his skin a shocking white in the grimy station light. He waves his blue-and-white shirt up and down and around in huge half-circles, performing an elaborate semaphore. She does not know whether to laugh or cry at his Italian-inspired passion for her, his exhibitionism, his never articulated need suddenly expressed to the entire train station. It is at moments like this she thinks he is a spoiled child.

She returns to Paris at the beginning of August, just a few days before the outbreak of the cataclysmic World War I. The private war between Bea and Modi is also just about to begin.

Artistic Scenes minus landscape and only the slightest suggestion of nudity:

*Marevna Vorobev, the Russian painter and former lover of Modigliani, is eyewitness to one of their rows. She writes:

We were all gathered one evening in Montmartre to see Max Jacob, Modigliani, and Mrs. Hastings. Ehrenburg, the Russian poet and journalist, and his wife, Katya; André Delhay, writer and philosopher; Paul Cornet, sculptor; Mitrani, the Greek philosopher, with Carmen, a girl from Montparnasse; me with Diego Rivera. For a while things were tame enough: Mitrani and Carmen, both drunk somewhat, making love on the sofa; Max Jacob and Delhay standing near the bureau discussing poetry and philosophy; Ehrenburg, Katya and myself singing Russian songs (or rather shouting them, for none of us had much of a voice); Rivera detached and jolly, eating sandwiches. Modigliani and Beatrice Hastings, far gone in drink, began one of their arguments. It quickly turned into a fight, with the two of them pommeling and kicking each other. They went at each other like fishwives. The next thing we knew, he had seized her and hurled her through the closed window. A shattering of glass, a scream, and all that remained visible of Beatrice Hastings was her legs dangling from the windowsill, the rest of her in the garden. Everyone rushed from the room to go to her assistance. Excited, Mirani and Carmen ran off to the far end of the garden to be alone. Hastings was carried in and laid on the sofa. Her long, flat breasts were daubed in blood; she was sober now, and wretched. She wept while Modigliani repeated 'Non mea culpa, non mea culpa.' He covered her in scotch plaid and began to comfort her, lovingly. When we left much later, Modi was methodically tearing strips of wallpaper off the wall, singing 'Capelli biondi, Vestiti bianco', which amazed me.

Next month, they are invited to the Quartz' Arts ball. Beatrice complains to him she has nothing to wear (although this is not likely). She puts on a delicate neutral silk dress. [Another version of the story says she wears an old black silk dress and complains it is out of fashion.] *He announces he will solve her problem.*

He proceeds to strategically shorten the dress, lengthen the V below her neckline, create small openings to reveal flesh. Using coloured chalk he garnishes the dress with butterflies, leaves, vivid flowers, dabs of yellow and red, up and down the skirt, buttocks, breasts, legs, ankles, bodice, ta- da, she is transformed: Titania, Queen of the Fairies.

Her dress enchants everyone at the ball. Drunk, unlikely anyone thinks of Modi as Oberon, King of the Fairies, although like Oberon he is elfish and very handsome.

It is also unknown whether this actually happened, or if it is part of the Modigliani legend created by the poet André Salmon after Modigliani's death.

** Part of what fuels Modi's rage at Beatrice is suspicion. Before meeting Modigliani, it is no secret she notches her conquests on the back of her bedpost. He also knows and hates he is a kept man. He resents the *cavalier servant* role she casts for him.

He is a mystery to himself when drunk or drugged, or both. Wears rage and drunkenness to mask his TB? His drunken mask, "a face to meet the faces? " He cares little if his rages contradict him.

His inability to sell his work or be appreciated is humiliating and another log on his funeral pyre, another disappointment that fuels his rage.

** His time with Beatrice is when he gives up sculpture, and for the rest of his remaining years paints and paints, the lines in his painting emerging spontaneously and inspired by Toulouse Lautrec, especially the nudes. His paintings gain in confidence. There is an intensity of colour; his lines appear natural and effortless. In his portraits he seeks to express, sardonically or vividly (sometimes simultaneously), the internal and external selves of his sitters. Their inner and outer reality. He aims at expressing the essential characteristics or core of his subjects. Truth unmasked, although oddly the faces in his paintings appear to be masks. He cares little if his work contradicts him.

**After two years of drunken fights, poetry (she blames Lautré-mont for his self- destructive poses), mad love, and cocaine and/or hashish nights, Beatrice decides living with Modi is bad for her health, nor can he be helped or saved from himself. She needs to be saved from him she thinks. His sentimental generosity irritates her. He often sells his paintings for next to nothing, or gives them away for a drink and a smile. He refuses to find a job to help support his painting. Beatrice no longer sees his drunken temper and volcanic fury as part of his artistic personality or passion. His anger exhausts her. She alternates between tears and exasperation, and as so often happens near the end of a relationship, what was once considered charm is now a source of contempt.

** Beatrice starts an affair with Alfredo Pina, another handsome Italian sculptor, though not as talented as Modi, nor is he as abusive and self-destructive.

She finds and takes the bohemian men she wants, she says to friends.

**Marie Vassilieff, the proverbial gruff little old woman with a heart of gold, runs an artists' canteen (more of a soup kitchen) on an ugly little street off Avenue du Maine in Montparnasse. Modigliani is one of her favorite customers. She often allows him to eat for free and provides him with a stipend of fifty centimes a day: "*Pour amore,*" she says, "*le visage d'amore.*"

She decides to hold a soirée for the Cubist painter Georges Braque, recently returned from the front with a head wound and awarded the Legion of Honour and Croix de Guerre for gallantry. She plans to invite everyone who is anyone, including her other special friends: Picasso, Juan Gris, Cendrars, Matisse, Max Jacob, their wives and girlfriends; thirty-five guests in total…but there is a rather large fly in the ointment. Beatrice insists on bringing Alfredo Pina. Beatrice is now attached to Pina but it is not clear if Modigliani knows, and to avoid an awkward situation (or one of Modi's well-known rages), Marie decides it is best not to invite Modigliani and offers him three francs not to attend, rather than the usually fifty centimes.

At the end of the meal, the door bursts open and a band of artists and models tumble into the canteen, including Modigliani. Pina spots Modigliani in the crowd and draws a revolver; a shot is fired. Screams, shouts, follow. Vassilieff in her memoirs claims she then grabbed Pina's wrist and pulled the revolver out of his hand. This does not seem possible given her age and stature. Someone (or perhaps several guests) did manage to remove the revolver from Pina, and others pushed Modigliani safely out the door.

In a memoir elsewhere, Modigliani is thrown down the stairs in a rage.

Beatrice and Modigliani's relationship is effectively over with an operatic "bang."

Pina's shot missed. Bullet stopped by an overcoat hanging in the hallway, to everyone's relief. The police were never informed.

Later, Beatrice confessed she was the one who gave Pina the revolver. She feared Modigliani's jealousy, violent incomprehensible rage. "It was not as if he was faithful to me. He bedded my pretty French-Canadian friend, Simone Thiroux, when I asked her to look after Modigliani while I was away in London," she said.

** Alfredo Pina, to his chagrin, is soon replaced by Beatrice with the young eighteen-year-old poet and future novelist Raymond Radiguet, who in turn shortly leaves her for Jean Cocteau, Jack of all Arts, poet, writer, designer, playwright, artist, and filmmaker.

** After Beatrice leaves him, Modigliani returns to the Bateau-Lavoir and resumes his heavy drinking, eats little, and eventually catches influenza. He tries to hide the rose-coloured spots of blood in his handkerchief after he coughs from the Eastern European painter Soutine. Soutine finds him ill, unable to get out of bed. Returning the help and friendship Modigliani provided him when he first arrived in Paris, Soutine nurses Modi back to health.

Simone Thiroux, the quiet, tall, pretty blonde enchanted by the artists of Montparnasse and now penniless (she quickly spent the small inheritance left to her by her parents), meets Modigliani again after his health recovers, at Chez Rosalie. A few short months later she is pregnant.

Multiples of Me:
I am a handsome elegant Italian young man
So lordly, so cultivated, so exquisite, so kind-hearted
Lover, artist, even-tempered, distinguished
Corrupted by Paris, corrupted by Lautréamont

I am an unbearable buffoon,
I cannot stand or keep away from alcohol
The weak author of my own downfall
Ruined by drugs, by La Vie Boheme, by poetry
By an indulgent mother, by artists, by masks

I am the most literate painter in all of Montparnasse
I memorize Dante, Leopardi, Villon, Baudelaire, Nietzsche

I am psychic and follower of Nostradamus
I believe the artist is an aristocrat of feeling
Reject in no particular order: Renoir's aesthetic of caressing buttocks
(*The Large Bathers*), Rodin, the light in Nice
Picasso and the Cubist crowd, Futurists, bourgeois domesticity,
Systems of power, narrative paintings, background

I am the painter everyone remembers after the world made famous.
I am the painter made famous by disaster, failure, and my Garsin
irony.

Art, Amedeo Modigliani:
My obsessive need for the reality of art
Excludes everything else
How can I explain?
My diverse selves become one under the spell of art
Everything removed except for sensations
Thrilling and seeking release.
Eye, heart, and hand form a united current
To ignore the power of art
Is a type of sleepwalking
Necessary to plant potatoes
March on straight roads.
Art is essence made image
You can see it in an African mask
Primitive flame like sex that transforms and remains itself
Creates what is already there if you dare to see
Recreates a mask for you to be. Caresses the heart.
Oh, I am weary tonight, repeat myself
Time to leave this café and the babble of inferiors.

Livorno Diary #6: Notes Towards and Away from an Answer

I left Casa Modigliani a little disappointed. I was expecting something original and real from the past: say, a pen, notebook, or even a few drawings, a desk, perhaps pots and pans, bed, but other than the original four rooms and flooring there is nothing preserved or on display from the family's past. The rooms are intact and vacant. Mute. There is nothing "personal" in the rooms.

The handwriting on his letters home or to friends (copies), and even one announcing his promise to marry Jeanne Hébuterne (I photographed it with my phone), is done in a hasty scrawl and in French, and looks like the script of a man in a hurry or indifferent to communicating with mere mortals.

The Casa is neat and tidy. Prints of his paintings and copies of his photos are mounted in a semi-scholarly way: laminated, crowded together, and lovingly placed on the walls as if you are visiting your daughter's work at the Science Fair.

The lack of original paintings or sculptures is not surprising, given the current value of his work.

The street corner and the opening to Via Roma is identical to the one at the time of Modigliani's birth. Two five-storey, vertical blocks stand on both sides of the street, and the location of the windows, brickwork and stone molding, small wrought-iron-fenced balconies, are all unchanged.

Instead of the clatter of carts and clip-clop of hooves, there is now the buzz of traffic. The debt collector's wagon would have waited and waited and left almost empty-handed near the exact same door.

Next, I find the last Modigliani residence on Via Leonardo Cambini (where there is a plaque to his Socialist brother Giuseppe Modigliani). I then decide to wander down Via Giovanni Marradi, a block over.

It is a sunny midday in the middle of the week near the end of October. The sunshine feels warm. The thin, grey shadows of people, thick store awnings and long streetlamps all fall on the pavement. Everyone is out running towards or away from errands and shopping. Women enter and leave small niche clothing stores; a pharmacy sign blinks on and off; students spill out of a bar, eating brioche; a lone pigeon lands on the sidewalk, pecks at something on the ground and flutters off; the traffic moves to and fro—but not talking of Modigliano. Buses growl, gasp; cars and motor scooters climb in and out of loud whinny octaves; a smell of fresh pastry and light cologne mingles in the air above the sidewalk. The entire street scene ordinary and full of unassuming little gestures.

I stop at a fish store and deli for a light lunch that bills itself as selling street food. The fried cod is delicious—*Baccala*—served with one large lemon wedge, a Mediterranean salad, and two fresh slices of Italian white bread. The cod is so good I even eat the skin. Refreshed, I continue down the street and eventually cross over into a quiet residential neighborhood dusted with umbrella pines, their tops a vivid green in the golden afternoon light, and wander into what turns out to be *Il Parco della Villa Fabbricotti*, the Villa Fabbricotti park.

The villa inside the park is open and is now the *Biblioteca Labronica,* the Labronica Library. Near the entrance on my left is a study hall with desks; on my right, a room with a desk, seated behind which is what appears to be the librarian; and directly in front of me is a marble staircase with a classically draped Ancient Greek or Roman female statue midway up the stairs, hand out, gesturing or begging. I decide to seat myself in the dimly lit study hall and write down some notes about the morning.

Modigliani never smiles in any of his photographs, except for one where he is standing beside a gesturing Picasso. Picasso's arms are in the air, fists clenched, looking straight at Jean Cocteau or André Salmon. It appears he is telling them an amusing story or good joke. Modigliani is off to the side, his face not looking back at the camera but smiling at Picasso. It is a candid shot and he clearly enjoys the moment.

In all his other photos, especially the portraits, he wears a haunted look. You can even see the decline in his face and eyes: the drugs, booze, poor living conditions, and his illness are all taking a steady toll on his frail body. It was already a weak body even before he got to Paris.

His portrait photos also suggest melancholy or sadness and quiet torment, yet he is stoic and unflinching in his desire to take on the monolith called Art, to defy and scorn fashion.

Modigliani's suffering and devotion to artistic purity is at times exasperating. He squanders his strength and health in acts of resistance or defiance.

He deliberately sabotages himself over and over again, either by generosity or recklessness.

Why? You wonder if it is a vain form of self-masochism. You wonder if it is the crazy Garsin blood. You wonder how he decided to be so cavalier about his life. You wonder about the academic phrase a victim of 19th century French and German Heroic Romanticism. You wonder if it is all a mask, as some biographers have suggested, covering up from family and friends the fact he had TB. Part of the answer includes that he must have recognized at some point that he was dying.

*He is an artistic Janus: one face looks forward, seeks acceptance, recognition, financial success; the other face stares in the opposite direction, rejects bourgeois comfort, morality, fame.

Creation is his only truth, released by drink; the movements and gestures in, out, towards painting, shaping volume, finding and realizing the human image in front of him, creating beauty for a world he believed no longer cared for it.

*"While painting he became so engrossed that, sometimes," attested Lunia, "he talked to her in Italian, a language she did not know."

*I have spent part of the last few days trying to sneak up on Modigliani, on Livorno, to catch something of him and the city unaware. It feels as if I am trying to catch shadows.

Unlike many other Italian towns and cities, much of old Livorno was bombed during WW II. The red-bricked Renaissance remains of the *Fotrezza Nuova,* New Fortress, sit, quiet and forlorn, in the harbour. Nearby is the small Piazza Micheli, and in the centre is the *Monument dei Quattro Mori,* Monument of the Four Moors. There are four Moors in chains, with Lord Ferdinando standing above them on a pedestal. The monument was completed in 1626 to commemorate the victories of Ferdinando I of Tuscany over the Ottomans. It is in remarkably good shape. The beautiful Terrazza Mascagni, spread out like a magnificent outdoor ballroom, black-and-white tiles, overlooks the sun-drenched sea, south of the monument. Here, a newlywed Chinese couple are being photographed.

Lining Viale Italia are outdoor restaurants where sketchy middle-aged Russian men and their Prada-dressed girlfriends try to eat pasta by hanging it off their forks above their open mouths to the nearby waiter's amusement. They appear to be baby birds trying to feed themselves worms.

And there are the tall palm trees. They stand ripe with yellow dates under their bright, wide green fronds all along Viale Italia, the main road on the water's edge that slavishly follows the coastline. Finally, there is the small Piazza Giuseppe Emmanuele Modigliani and fountain, named for his famous socialist, anti-fascist brother. It is also on Viale Italia.

All of this does not satisfy what I am looking for or at: the intersection of past and present.

I now realize what I hope to find is only possible in a dream, a painting or book, which, when all is said and done, are all forms of oneiric consciousness. It is probably why I needed to write this book. It is what poetry and film do best.

Reality is boring, that is why I prefer fiction.
—François Truffaut

When painting, he often declaimed Dante, Verlaine, Rimbaud, or hummed, lips pressed, throughout the whole session. He would sometimes burst out laughing in the middle of it all.
—Hanka Cirowska, wife of Leopold Zborowski, Modigliani's last art dealer

Part Five: New Lovers:
Simone Thiroux and Jeanne Hébuterne

1917

Simone Thiroux, model & lover:
I moved to Paris at the age of twenty-one
Orphaned early, I left my aunt and Quebec
For freedom, laughter, art, and a medical degree.
Before the war, my low-cut dresses and breasts,
And I danced and laughed, gave and spent money.
We watched the early morning sun
Rise in the east behind the Tour Eiffel
Mist float off the Seine.
We talked of love, art, artistic tempers
Dined with artists at Chez Rosalie's
Poor Beatrice and I and lovely Modi.
Now look at me and my misfortune:
Scar above my right eye after a jealous fight
At the Rotonde between Beatrice and him
Consumptive fever, pregnant with his child.
The painting before my troubles captures my sad, pale-blue eyes
Blonde-red hair, two different earrings and pale skin
Another is me standing nude, modest, quiet, and passive
My head titled to the right, cheeks rouged
Same pale blue eyes, yes, only painted smaller
My perfect round breasts he called answered prayers

2

Our baby is born, and I love with all my heart
I write to you now to ask, beg
To see you from time to time
Swear on the head of our child I forgive you
My only fault is I love too much and suffer.

I do not ask for money, earn my own living
I only ask for a little less hate, console me.
A crumb of your affection would make me so happy
Do me so much good, I am dying
Tuberculosis is doing its work
I feel nothing but tenderness for you.
Write and tell me you are well and want to see me
I am caught by my desire for you.

March 1917

Simone Thiroux is seven months pregnant when Modigliani meets Jeanne Hébuterne. It is five weeks before Jeanne's eighteenth birthday. He is thirty-two. It is half a year, more or less, after the Braque banquet, the abrupt departure of Beatrice Hastings, and "the shooting," what the poet and critic Max Jacob records in his journal as *scenes avec revolvers.*

In a letter to a friend, Hébuterne writes that Modigliani took her to the Hotel Dieu. She ends up with her underclothes torn. She notes it was far from being a sensual romantic evening *avec* the famed rebel artist and lover of Montparnasse. Instead, it was a night "without a certain horror," a dark Lautréamont suggestion (sadistic?) on the edge of their relationship (in the centre?) at the start of their affair. Later, she sneaks off from Breton, where the family is on holiday, to see him again, in spite of the suggestion earlier that the affair got off to a far from genteel romantic start.

Their liaisons continue for over a year without her parents' knowledge.

She spends her days with Modigliani, attends art classes, and in the evening dutifully returns to her parents' home. Occasionally, she spends the night, telling her parents she is staying with friends.

By the spring of 1918, the affair is no longer a secret. She is unable to conceal her pregnancy from her mother. Nor can the affair be quashed, despite her parents' objections about the unsuitability of Modigliani.

Quiet, dependable, loyal, affectionate, and an art student, Hébuterne is the emotional and practical ballast Modigliani needs in his life.

She, for her part, seems to appreciate or share with him his secret sexual tastes.

In appearance, she resembles a woman who has walked out of a Pre-Raphaelite painting: long, dark brown hair past her shoulders, with red and gold highlights; smoldering, coquettish eyes; youthful, smooth skin. She is thin and tiny, and appears both vulnerable and ethereal. Her facial expression: vague, bewitching, and fey. There are Gothic traces, hints, in the flirty, mysterious expression she gives, looking back from the photograph.

The Japanese painter and Modigliani's artistic comrade-in-arms in Montparnasse, Foujita, called her *vicieuse et sensuelle*, vicious and sensual.

July 1917

Thiroux gives birth to a baby boy she calls Gérard.

She writes to Modigliani eight months later, ill with TB, hoping for some kind of reconciliation before she dies. She does not seem to be aware that at this point Modigliani is also suffering from tuberculosis, or at the very least a bronchial condition returned from his youth. He does not reply. He refuses to acknowledge the child and tells everyone she is an amoral bitch who slept with anyone and everyone. Dismisses his paternity and comments: "So what would I have done with this baby? Someone like me, who has never had a penny, was I made to be a father of a family?"

Gérard is later adopted. As an adult, he becomes a priest, and never acknowledges Modigliani as his father.

Thiroux is one of the many who walks in Modigliani's funeral procession through Montparnasse to the cemetery. She dies heartbroken a year later, in 1921, of TB, the same suspected killer of Modigliani.

*Jeanne and Simone are similar: "a peculiar poverty of spirit marked each of them." Both quiet, passive, stoic young women.

Leopold Zborovski, Art Dealer:
I heard about him before we actually met
His transformation from polite *bello ragazzo*
To louche, penniless Prince of Montparnasse
Former lover of Anna Akhmatova, Nietzsche, tasteful clothes
Heard how they sat together in the warm summer rain
Under his enormous battered black umbrella
On a bench in the Luxembourg Garden and recited Verlaine
Delighted to discover each remembered the same stanzas.
The man's soul is romantic, which never earns,
I suggested he try nudes.
They arrived after some sunless days in an empty room
Empty bottle, dirty collar, colourless eyes and a warm smile
He threw back thick curtains in a quick generous sweep
Painted her on a red blanket without a mask, eyes shut
Colour like Eden's first morning light imagined
Each curve touched and weighted by quicksilver apprehension.
You are a sensual, provocative but orderly lover
I remarked after seeing the distant masked face, full breasts
A lifetime of fears, doubts, hopes, and rage
Now made profitable.

Zbo, Beautiful Nudes:

Modigliani painted thirty-five or thirty-nine nudes between 1916 and 1919. Things are seldom precise when tracking my friend Modigliani. The vast majority were done from 1916-17 on my request. I locked him up every day with a naked model and a bottle. Imagine! I paid him fifteen francs a day, plus covered his expenses for paints, canvas, and a model.

He completed two nudes in 1918 and managed to finish three in 1919. Illness. TB?

Here is a partial catalogue of nudes completed by Modigliani between 1916 and 1919:

> Nude on Sofa (Almaisa, Algerian model), 1916
> Female Nude, 1916
> Reclining Nude with arms folded under her head, 1916
> Seated Female Nude (Iris Tree, actress and model), 1916
> Blonde Nude (Simone Thiroux), 1917
> Le Grand Nu, 1917
> Lying Nude, 1917
> Nude Seated on a Sofa, 1917
> Reclining Nude, 1917
> Nude with a Necklace, 1917
> Nude on a Blue Cushion, 1917
> Reclining Nude, 1917
> Sleeping Nude with arms open (The Red Nude), 1917
> Venus Nude, 1917
> Standing Nude (Simone Thiroux), 1917
> Seated Nude, 1918
> Seated Nude with folded hands, 1918
> Elvira, 1918

Nude (x3), 1919.

Modigliani paints the same model three times (No. 19) in the same posture, changing only the hair colour, background colours, the bulk and colour of the cushion she rests her head on.
Health alas, was not on his side.
Although this is a partial list, it does give you, madame, a general idea of the vast and varied Modigliani nudes available.

Let me assure, each nude is done with exquisite taste, without a hint of impropriety or vulgar suggestion. There is, let us say, an uninhibited pleasure without indecency in a woman's body in his work. Compare him to Courbet's *Origin of the World* to see what I mean.

Each nude is individual. The eyes, hair, body type, posture, colouring, are unique to the specific model. I believe, if I dare to say, many of the nudes express a magnificent mischief, foreign women or otherwise. Note the fine gold/orange colouring, the full round breasts on, say, *The Seated Nude*. Note also the sly, mysterious glances in some, or the invitation to admire, or the quiet erotic slumber in others. The natural elegant flow of the line, the caress of the brush. Intimate, like the French language spoken in bed by a charming French woman at one a.m. This is a sensual painter who clearly loves women. He delights in the full-length view of a woman—so unlike Renoir, obsessed with round, gauzy derrières, or the new upstart Picasso, who transforms women into a geometry experiment. Where is the beauty in that, I ask you? Love? Caught desire?

*"When Modigliani was doing the nudes, primarily at 3 rue Joseph-Bara (Zborowski's residence), Zborowski would slip in; his motive obvious, Modigliani's more complicated. Modigliani would then fly into a rage. Once while painting *Red Nude*, one of his greatest nudes, Zborowski came in and Modigliani threatened to throw the model down the stairs, naked, and destroy the picture. Thus, his sessions with the nudes had something of the intimacy of sexual love apart from the consummation, a knock on the door sufficient to disrupt."

*Unlike the portraits, all his nudes are painted with clear, visible eyes. The nudes look back at you with an impish, merry sparkle, or the eyes are shut in sleep or modesty, mouths firmly set, and some simply stare back at you, frankly.

Both the model's face and the viewer participate and celebrate in the unmasking of the body, celebration of the body. Modigliani's nudes are sensual, fleshy, and direct. They exist on the canvas by themselves, for themselves, and seem to wink at or invite you in.

Léopold Zborowski: Modigliani's last art dealer

** Modigliani leaves Paul Guillaume, his second art dealer, in June 1916 (pre-war, Paul Alexandre was his first), for Leopold Zborowski, his last art dealer. Guillaume is a penny-pincer and this infuriates Modigliani. Nor is he able to sell his portraits. They quarrel often. Modigliani does an ironic portrait of Paul Guillaume in 1915. Head titled back, dressed in a fashionable brown jacket, high white collared shirt and cravat, hat on a jaunty angle, face and chin squeezed together as if just finished sucking on a lemon. He looks sour. Face pinched.

Guillaume does not like the rendering of himself and refuses to buy it from him. The sardonic intent is obvious. They shrug each other off.

** Leopold Zborowski is a Polish émigré. He arrives in Paris in 1913 after studying literature at the University of Cracow, and leads a dissipated life, much like Modigliani, until he marries Anna (*Hanka*, in Polish) Cirowska, the daughter of a wealthy, aristocratic Polish family.

He turns his focus away from cocaine and poetry after marrying, and takes up the career of art dealer, based primarily on his passion for art. He is an idealist, generous, and impractical, his head often in the clouds, especially in his relationship with Modigliani. Unlike Guillaume, he is an outsider in French society art circles.

Zbo, his nickname, believes Modigliani is "twice as good as Picasso" and recruits Modigliani after seeing a performance at the Lyre and Palette on 6 rue Huygens in the 14th arrondissement where Modigliani was also showing some work in the gallery (but not selling).

It is Zbo who sets in motion Modigliani's nude period and from whom he gets his second wind. Zbo's method is simple: He locks Modi in a room with paints, canvas, model, and drink, and at the end of the day there is a completed nude portrait.

Paintings begin to pile up. He stacks them in a cold, narrow room without furniture, smelling of candle wax, on 3 rue Joseph-Bara.

**Modigliani tells Zbo:

> I want my life to be one, each part feeding or infusing the other, and not to exist in two separate spheres, the dream and the real. To create is to want, to wait, to make gestures towards a dream until the dream and the real co-exist, the boundary never completely disappearing but blurred, indistinct, the real and the dream infusing each other.
>
> The magic of art, like any revelation, appears and disappears like sunlight on water, moves like small waves on the beach forward, backward. Gone.
>
> You seem to understand this. You also dream with your eyes open.

** Zbo arranges a one-man exhibition of Modigliani's nudes from December 3 to 30, 1917, at the Berthe Weill Gallery on 50 rue Taitbout. Mlle. Weill is a feisty and eccentric gallery owner. She already has had success with avant-garde artists when she hosted a show in 1901 of Fauve artists and Matisse.

She hangs one of Modigliani's more sumptuous nudes in the front window to generate public interest. The painting draws a crowd, and complaints about pubic hair.

The same day the show opens, she is ordered by the police to take down the offensive painting, and the remaining nudes off the walls inside the gallery. Pubic hair in public is named the villain.

Two drawings are sold for thirty francs each. Mlle.Weill buys five paintings out of pity and consideration for Zborowski and Modigliani's efforts after the show is shut down.

Modigliani's one and only show devoted exclusively to his work during his lifetime ends in personal and financial failure.

** Zbo spits, curses Modigliani's soul-crushing fate.

** Forty miles northwest of Paris, men are being slaughtered daily as trench warfare roars on, each side hoping for a major breakthrough. Butchered, shattered, handsome young men lie in the mud; beautiful, sensual young women lie nude on blankets and cushions. Horrible ironic symmetry.

Jeanne Hébuterne:
It is easier to tell you how it began than to tell you why it continues. I was in the Colarossi Art Academy on rue de la Grande-Chaumière, waiting my turn to paint or sketch the nude model, something I can hardly afford on my own.

I did not see him enter the studio, but there he was beside me, like a magician.

—Are you an artist?

—Yes. No. I am an art student. I have only done a few pieces.

—But, you have the heart of an artist. It is easy to see. Your pretty eyes, eyes of an observer.

He then smiled his beautiful smile. His handsome face shone on me like the morning sun. The effect was extraordinary. I felt immediately 'sympathic' towards him. Yes, his clothes were shabby, a vague odor of wine, cigarette smoke, a sweet/sour smell. Simultaneously, there was his beau visage, his gentle courtesy, the sing-song way he spoke French. My heart soared.

—Are you an artist, Monsieur?

—Of course, Mademoiselle. I ignore landscape painting. Instead, I paint beautiful nudes. I have no use for the current geometry they call Cubism. Hence, I am poor and ignored. Alas, I am another one of Picasso's victims.

He smiled. Nodded towards the model.

—She has firm, pretty tits. Her areolae look like brown shields. Nice curve on her hips. I like her jawline and eyes. Someone should tell her to trim her hairy pussy.

I blushed but noted his keen artistic eye.

His frankness was refreshing. His eyes seemed to know and understand my quiet longing. My life. I am caught. My desire, my confusion to be someone else other than plain, stubborn Jeanne Hébuterne. To be transformed by art. To soar above my bourgeois upbringing, listening to my father scold us with Pascal.

He knows many artists in Montparnasse. My appalling ex-lover, the Japanese artist Foujita, with thin lips and a hairless cock, a drinking companion. Modi does not care for his portraits. Cold and lifeless. Frigid innocence, he says. Prefers the mad Bulgarian painter, Pascin. Wonderful, alive nudes. Pascin likes to paint lesbian scenes. A charming man.

You see, Modigliani was a wounded songbird sitting on my shoulder, singing freedom.

I wanted him. The artistic life. I was shaking. Is it possible to feel this way so swiftly, I asked myself?

We were soon making love, taking love, giving love. Wanting love. Smashing love. Shedding masks.

He had no patience for false modesty. Tore my underclothing in two, our first time. Plunged his tongue into me. Then slapped my outer lips quickly, one blow followed by the other. Tongue pushed hard against the sting. The mixture of pleasure and pain bewildering, yet it transported me. A lion opening my gates.

He plunged without mercy.

The more we made love, the quieter I became. My soul soared, united with him in the dark. He found in me what I did not know I desired.

But, outwardly, I was calm, busy with my studies. Happy. He called me his 'petit haricot,' little bean. Sometimes, after our lovemaking, I sat, the closed window my mirror, and brushed my hair that fell to the top of my naked hips.

He softly called to me from the bed: Mademoiselle Rossetti, mon belle, your prince adores you. It was our agreed signal. I turned. I was proud he possessed me. In grand style, I parted my fess cleft to him.

I used to torment boys my age. Give them just enough to hear the tightening of their breath. See them pull their stomach upright and stiff.

I knew they were stirred, felt their excitement. Enjoyed their restrained quivering thrusts against my thigh. I pushed them away, smiling.

Left them with a marine scent on their fingers. Went home and finished what they started, pleased with myself and my ability to create desire.

Learning to be a woman, I thought. Searched their eyes the next day in the classroom and I knew I could possess them. All I learned as a girl did not matter with Modi. I discovered beauty in his darkness. We lived for each other. We traded secrets. He brought light to my darkness.

Then I became pregnant with his child.

The truth is, he is my first god. It does not matter I am no longer his goddess.

It touches me deeply how much he dotes on our baby.

I have no illusions. I know he sleeps with his models, but he always comes home to me. It is necessary for his art. His rage in the café over, drunk, two a.m., he comes home to me. We sit together for hours on a bench, his arm around my shoulders, without a word, the holy silence of love protecting us.

He is everything to me: father, brother, husband, fiancé.

Part Six: The Light in Nice, April 1918

The Germans bombed the outskirts of Paris with their artillery and planes in January 1918. Everyone was nervous: what will happen next. Will our line hold? Is this a prelude to an unstoppable invasion and defeat? Then, to make matters worse, the art market collapsed in April, and then the Spanish influenza swept through Paris. Shortly after this another calamity: Modi fell ill with the flu.

I decided the best course of action was to take him and some other artists out of Paris and kill two birds with one stone. The French Riviera with its clean, fresh, salty air is a tonic. The endless warm, bright, sunny days a counterpoint to the cold and damp of Paris.

It would help to revive Modi's health, I reasoned. Raise our spirits. I also hoped he and Soutine and Foujita would paint some landscapes à la mode Fauvist, which sold so well, eventually, only a few years ago. There were many idle and wealthy British aristocrats spending their days dining, reading newspapers, strolling on the Promenade des Anglais, gambling at the Hotel Negresco in the evenings, arching an eyebrow over lunch. I would only need a few of them to buy, to recover my expenses. Several sales, and there would be a tiny profit. Modi's nudes an additional enticement.

So, we set off by train: Hanka, my wife; Modi and Jeanne, pregnant, and her mother Eudoxie (she finally accepted Jeanne's choice, I thought); Modi's friend and fellow painter, Soutine; Foujita and his new bride, Fernande Barrey—the dear had worked as a prostitute before turning to painting at Soutine's encouragement, and was a model for many artists including Modi.

I should have understood there would be tension and animosity in this group. My wife Hanka blames my lack of foresight on my dreamy apprehension of reality. Zbo, you are a soft touch when it comes to artists. I tell Hanka I knew about Barrey's past, but I did not expect it to assert itself in the present and create jealousy between Soutine and Foujita. And how was I to know Foujita was the one who had deflowered Jeanne? They were briefly lovers before she met

Modi. Modi smouldered with suppressed rage whenever he was in Foujita's presence, on the verge of exploding at any moment. He is proud and refuses to be thought of as a cuckold.

Jeanne's mother, Eudoxie, quarreled violently with Modi whenever the two of them spent more than half an hour in each other's company. I underestimated her anxiety about her daughter's poor choice of husband.

She called Modi an "unsuitable alcoholic." She accused him of robbing the cradle—and, worse, her daughter was expecting a child and still not married.

Modi refused to accept her criticism and shouted back she was nothing but a loud, yappy, petty, bourgeois cunt. "You know nothing about me or your daughter. It is all about appearances, all about sham appearances for you."

I was forced to keep them apart, which suited Modi just fine. Pregnant Jeanne and Eudoxie took an apartment on rue Massena. It was the only way to keep the peace. Modi would only meet with Jeanne in the morning and they would take coffee together. He then escorted her to the tram, and she would go back to her mother. His true daily attachment, of course, was his art.

Soutine added to my headaches. Henka warned me about smelly Soutine and his habits, but Modi convinced me to bring him to Nice, his only "true" friend. Soutine rarely bathed, complained of the light and heat, and was prone to violent, stubborn outbursts at the slightest remark about his art, work habits, or money. Foujita called him "the Lizard" for spending most of his time sleeping in the sun. Soutine's only real interest was his monthly stipend—I sometimes was late in providing it and this enraged him—and I was barely able to control my own resentment and anger. He did nothing all day, most days.

Soutine wanted to return to the urban hum and buzz of Paris, the beehive of human activity. He could not paint what I had hoped. Cagnes, the sleepy town the artists had settled in outside of Nice, was unbearable to him. He wrote to me, "The landscape is something I cannot endure... I will soon be forced to do some miserable still lifes."

The heat of July eventually forced everyone's hand. Soutine and Foujita and his wife retuned to Paris, but Modi stayed on and mainly concentrated on portraits.

After so many years in Paris, the light in Nice was unbearable to his new "Parisian" eyes. Modi did manage to squeeze out one good landscape, *Midi Landscape*, very much a Cézanne-themed composition: cypress trees, a tan hillside village, and green cultivated terraces march up the side of the hill. He also painted a series of portraits of the local servants and farmers, and two portraits of Jeanne. I was unable to sell any, including the nudes, but for the sake of his health, agreed to continue to pay for his stay in Provence and for him to pursuit our reckless dream. The dream, already a financial loss and an overwrought emotional burden. What could a few extra months do to make the situation worse?

The baby, Giovanna (Jeanne), was born November 29, 1918, a few weeks after the end of the war. My hope was that the birth of the baby would settle him down. Make him mindful of his health, drink less, and control his drunken rages (he can be the perfect gentleman when sober), perhaps smoke less. Apply himself to work in a steady, disciplined way, at least for the sake of his baby, without drugs or alcohol.

So, in early December, Eudoxie, Hanka and I returned to Paris with hopes of a new beginning. It was agreed Jeanne would find a wet nurse and I will help pay for her. The two of them are hopeless at looking after their baby, although he clearly adores her. Jeanne seems resigned to her fate.

The new year was just around the corner, the war over. I wished for the sake of all of us that the new year would bring a fresh start, the end of the war, the start of a better future after so much death and misery.

Needless to say, Modi's unerring ability to behave like a doomed man continued. Hanka simply thinks I am too kind and gullible when it comes to Modi.

** December 31, New Year's Eve, 1918, Modi sends the following telegram:

Dear Zbo,

I embrace you. I am hitting it up with Survage at the Coq d'Or. I have sold all my pictures. Send me some money soon.

Champagne is flowing like water.

Life resurrected.

This starts a new life. The New Year.

** A few days later:

Dear Zbo,

You are naïve and can't take a joke. I haven't sold a thing.

Now for something that is true and very serious.

My wallet with 600 francs has been stolen. You can imagine how upset I am...

Naturally, I am broke, or almost. It is all too stupid... Just when I thought I had found finally found a little peace.

I am also missing my identity card and travel documents to return to Paris. I recognize my blame (if there is blame) and my debt (if there will be debt) and we both agree I am a sinner and fool. Why can't you help me—and quickly—so as not to stop something that is going well? Do what you will—and can—but answer me, it's urgent. Time presses.

Mid-April 1919

Jeanne Hébuterne:
I am pregnant with my second child. Modi jokes and complains he is getting fat and becoming a respectable citizen, a proper bourgeois. He rolls his eyes in disbelief, throws his hands up in mock despair, and smiles. We will soon have two children—unbelievable, he says. I can't say I like his jokes.

He wants to return to the hell of Paris now that his health has improved. He longs for his late evenings in cafés; the soft grey light and sky of Paris; its liberated urgency now that the war is finally over.

The warm, colourful Mediterranean light is too powerful for him. Nice: too quiet, too provincial. He says Paris and company stimulates his work, and wishes to return in May.

Sadly, I am not enough for him. I worry we will never marry.

Max Jacob's Journal:

May 23, 1919
Modi is back from the south. I saw him the other day at La Rotonde and he looks well although he says his teeth still bother him and not more than once he coughed into his handkerchief and stained it a faint rose colour. He brushed away my alarm saying it is what was left of a spring flu. He told me he stopped drinking and aims to be more mindful of his health because he is now a father. His charm is on in full display as a father. The baby is called Jeanne or Giovanna in Italian. He delights in her blonde hair, full ruddy cheeks, her sparkling nutty brown eyes and sweet cooing mouth.

Jeanne, the mother of his child, is still in the south pregnant with their second child and not fit to travel back to Paris.

He is excited about his future. He is currently working hard for a show in the fall in London: Nine paintings and fifty drawings of his work will be exhibited.

I offered him my warm congratulations. He smiles his charming smile and says: 'Picasso is still a salad, (shit), Cubism a cadaver.'

May 28, 1919
Modi and Lunia Czechowska take long walks in the Luxembourg Garden. They have also been seen dining together at Chez Rosalie. She is pretty. Lunia and her husband Casmir are good friends of Leopold Zborowski, his art dealer, and with his wife Hanka.

Zbo tells me he is quite taken by her. She is thoughtful and kind and already he has done two portraits of her. He talks to her about how unlikely he will see his little girl grow up, how he longs to return to Livorno and be near his mother.

Zbo shakes his head and shouts out no when I ask him if Modi has started an affair with Lunia. I find this hard to believe. I know the man and his past affairs. Lunia for her part reports to Zbo she is amazed how his portraits 'expose my soul.' The stuff of chaste meeting of the minds? Mere friendship?

June 18, 1919
    The man is unpleasant, proud, angry, insensitive, wicked, and rather stupid, sardonic, and narcissistic.

July 10, 1919
    Jeanne sent a telegram to Zbo asking for train fare back to Paris. Modi is hopeless. She returned, two months pregnant, at the end of June. A few days later Modi signed a note written in French 'promising to marry Mlle Jane Hebuterne' as soon as his documents arrived from Italy. I assume it is his new identity papers. The promise to marry note was witnessed by Zbo and Lunia. A strange and curious turn of events. Especially odd is calling Jeanne, 'Jane.' Is this deliberate or a poor practical joke?
    Modi does not wear domesticity well. As for Jeanne, she can barely look after one baby and now a second. The current baby is staying with a nurse in the countryside outside Orleans. Jeanne visits her once a week.
    Jeanne is sullen and patient or something. It is impossible to say since whenever Modi is around working or talking she fades into the background and says next to nothing.

July 22, 1919
    Zbo says Modi still comes around to paint nudes at his apartment and works on portraits in his studio/home. His health continues to go up and down but in spite of his health works. He is possessed by a demon or genius. I would hazard a guess and say both. He paints until exhausted, covered in sweat and half-hatched from drink, and then takes his now famous bath.
    Jeanne's attempts, sadly, to reconcile with her parents have failed.
    Modi's exile from alcohol short-lived.
    They both cling to each other as if ship-wrecked.
    'What's Hecuba to him or he to Hecuba / That he should weep for her?' Perverse, dear journal.

August 1, 1919

Modi is ill and unable to travel to London for the exhibition at the Mansard Gallery featuring new French art: Derain, Picasso, Matisse, Modigliani, Soutine, Survage, Utrillo and Zadkine to name a few. His is the most represented with over fifty pieces. Zbo's handiwork. Zbo reports a few of his pieces sold. The Sitwells bought two paintings and the British critics responded favourably to his work in the press.

He sent the reviews to his mother including the French review in L'Eventail.

He continues to paint at a feverish pace whenever he rises Lazarus like from the bed.

August 19, 1919

His illness, like poetry or the erotic, marks him with a different sense of time (urgent), a separate reality from the everyday and prosaic. He is most alive when he paints and drinks. Sober he is a man drowning. He can see his own dead body. The pursuit of Beauty has always had its own tragic obligations.

October 15, 1919

Andre Utter, Susan Valadon's lover, and who is also the mother of Utrillo, tells this story. They were dining at Guerin's with friends when suddenly Modi turned up and joined them. He was, to Utter's surprise, relatively sober and in a quiet reflective mood. He only took one glass when offered. He sat beside Valadon, placed his head sad and gentle on her shoulder and said she was the only woman who understood him. Held her. He then began to sing a dirge—the Kaddish— mourning his own death.

October 22, 1919

Whenever Modi takes ill and the word gets out, art dealers call on Zbo to find out his status. They all want to buy up his art cheaply before he dies so they can profit from his death.

November 17, 1919

Evening. Modi and Utrillo drunk under Lunia's window. They sing, beg, for her to come down and open the door. Jeanne finds Modi the next morning naked sleeping in the nearby flower garden and Utrillo passed out and asleep under a bench. Not the first time Modi strips down in public. Known all over Montparnasse he likes to expose himself. He particularly likes to reveal his alabaster skin to elderly British women.

December 31, 1919–January 1920
    Drinking all day and into the morning with Greek composer, Mario Varogli and other Greek friends.
    Modi refuses to go home to Jeanne. He toasts the new year and to a new life. The unfinished portrait of Varogli, his last work, is on the easel.

January 10, 1920
    He is very ill. He joined a group of friends (after an argument with Jeanne?) the other day in the freezing rain and cold and refused to wear his overcoat. When they arrived at Benito's—a good twenty, twenty-five-minute walk—he refused their request to join them inside. Instead, he cursed Benito and sat on the wet boulevard raving he was on a quay before an imaginary sea. Three hours later they exited and found him sitting on a bench still in his short-sleeves. He said this was the most beautiful site on earth and he insisted he be left alone. He was waiting for a boat to ferry him to a miraculous country. But, what is this illness?
    Death cold, aloof and indifferent is now his mistress.
    Poetry, his theatrical villain, hides behind the stage curtain and waits. Wears a mask.

January 18, 1920

Lunia and Hanka washed and scrubbed for over two days the studio apartment on 8 rue de la Grande-Chaumière last summer before Modi and pregnant Jeanne moved in. It is on the same street as the Académie Colarossi where they first met.

The L-shaped studio is a study in opposites (like Modi and Jeanne). Hot as an oven in summer and frigid in winter if not heated. Water is only available from a single tap in the courtyard and needs to be carried up in a pail. One toilet for the entire building. They use candles and oil lamps for light.

Today, the pot coke stove is dead, blue coal box empty, room frigid. The brown floorboards and bed are covered with oily stains. The room is littered. Empty sardine tins and drained bottles. Fierce headache. Stiff neck. Hot fever. He lies on a stained pallet bed and moans, coughs, spits blood. Lungs hemorrhaging. Jeanne, stunned, sits beside him, overwhelmed. Silent despair in her stoic eyes. Grief has made her unable to think or move for three days. She never calls for a doctor. She remains motionless as a statue.

Zbo, home sick with the flu, has been unable to pay his customary visit. Hanka rushes home after her visit to tell him Modi is coughing up blood.

In the ambulance Modi murmurers to no one in particular, "I have only a fragment of brain left."

Hospital of Charity, January 24, 1920

**...*And then I hear the sea roaring in my ears, followed by the sweet, sickly taste of blood in my mouth. Sweat pours out of me. Burns, burns, my body burns...can you hear me? Cold, so cold. I can see mother crying. I am dead. Where are the coins for the ferry man? Speak, Jeanne,* *speak. I, my, chest broken. More brandy—anything. Blood on my tongue. Breathe. Cannot. So tired, tired, weary. I am a wounded albatross. So much silence. Lungs whistle. Tree branches in the wind. I see shadows. Leaves. Sunlight. More brandy. Wash away the taste of blood. Oh my chest…lift the stones off my chest, Jeanne. Cannot lift my broken wings. The gondolas of Venice wear black ribbons today. Why? Sea makes a deep, inhuman sound.*

Promise to follow me, dear wife… Italia! Cara, cara Italia!

The room was very still. He is unconscious. Kisling and Ortz, both artists and friends, had carried him down two flights of stairs from the studio, his arms slumped over their shoulders to the waiting ambulance below.

** The death certificate states Modigliani's cause of death is tubercular meningitis. Death slips off his mask. Others speculate his mask was never removed. TB?

Hébuterne's residence, January 25, 1920

Modigliani fell into a coma from which he never recovered; his last words "*Cara Italia.*" He dies at 8:45, the evening of January 24, 1920. Jeanne is let in to see him and she lets out a piercing scream—her only show of emotion the entire time he is ill—when she sees his dead body.

Zbo, Hanka and Lunia decide it is best if Jeanne does not return to the apartment on Grand-Chaumière, nor should she be left alone, almost nine months pregnant and grief-stricken. Zbo puts her up in a cheap hotel in Montparnasse with his young housekeeper, Paulette Jourdain, to keep her company and to keep an eye on her zombie-like composure. Everyone assumes she is in shock.

The next morning Jeanne's father comes to the hotel to collect his daughter and bring her, finally, home, regardless of her second pregnancy.

The Hébuternes live on the fourth floor of a house across from a long apartment block. The house and apartment block are separated by a large courtyard. Above their rooms on the fifth floor is a single bedroom. It is hoped it is here Jeanne's recovery will begin; the family start the process of reconciliation.

Her brother André remains with her in her room. At some point—around five a.m.—he dozes off, and Jeanne crawls out of bed, leans back and drops off the balcony to follow Modigliani. The position of the body shows she fell backward.

She lands with a dull thud. Back of the head smashed, one leg broken. It is a cold, grey morning, January 26, 1920. Her body is discovered at six a.m. by a worker in the courtyard. She was twenty-one.

** Kisling, and Moricand, another artist, decide to make Modi's death mask before the body is removed from the hospital to the morgue. They are rushed, and the result is a botched job. The plaster is removed before it hardens and, to their horror, pulls off bits of skin and hair. Later, another artist—Lipchitz—fixes the mess by casting the mask into bronze. Modigliani would appreciate the irony of the need to fix two different masks before finally casting one permanent one.

** Louis Libaude, unscrupulous art dealer for Utrillo and Valadon, rushes out and buys all the Modigliani drawings and paintings he can find when he hears of Modigliani's collapse. He begins to make an immense profit when Modi dies a few days later.

** The funeral procession, led by Leopold Zborowski and his wife Hanka, starts in rue Jacob on the Left Bank and makes its way across the Seine to Père Lachaise Cemetery on the Right Bank, a four-and-a-half-kilometre walk.

The procession includes many from the artistic communities of Montmartre and Montparnasse: Picasso, Brâncuși, Foujita, Soutine, Derain, Severini, Utter, Valadon, Max Jacob; all walk behind the horse-drawn casket covered with sumptuous floral wreaths. Diego Riviera does not attend. The funeral would interrupt his morning painting schedule. Lost in the crowd and quietly crying is the unknown and abandoned lover, Simone Thiroux.

**Simone Thiroux dies of TB a year later, 1921, age 23.

** Zbo prospered after Modigliani's death; he enjoyed attending the horse races outside Paris, fine clothes, and dining. He died suddenly of a heart attack at the age of 43, March 25, 1932.

**Paul Guillaume, Modigliani's first art dealer, shot himself October 1, 1934. He was also 43.

**Beatrice Hastings became an alcoholic, survived cancer, and then committed suicide by gas in October 30, 1943, in London. She was 64. It is rumoured she may have had Modi's baby and gave it up for adoption.

** Max Jacob was arrested by the Gestapo in February 1944, although he converted to Catholicism at an early age. He died March 5, 1944, in the infirmary near the Drancy internment camp, of bronchial pneumonia. He was 67.

** Picasso made and changed art history.

** Modigliani, at his death, was hailed as Prince of the Bohemians by his contemporaries. In a letter to Modigliani's brother Giuseppe, Zbo calls him "a son of the stars."

Livorno Diary #7: Somewhere beyond the surface of things.

My last day in Livorno. I decide to visit the Fattori Museum. It is, once again, a bright sunny day, the sky a spotless blue.

The Fattori Museum is in Villa Mimbelli, a grand, light-coloured limestone building built in the 19th century, surrounded by a few stout, drowsy palm trees just up the street from my B&B. To my dismay I arrive with a little more than an hour before closing time.

The museum is named after Giovanni Fattori, who was part of the Macchiaioli art movement and a teacher to Micheli who, in turn, was one of Modigliani's art teachers. Modigliani learned a sense of solidity of form in his paintings from Micheli and from working on sculptures. Modigliani's lines possess an additional feature. They have what D.H. Lawrence saw in the tomb drawings of the Etruscans: "the quick, vital, joyous pulse of life itself" (see the Etruscan tomb frescoe *The Two Dancers* or *The Swimmer*). The lines in Modigliani's portraits, nudes, or drawings are put down in one quick, vital apprehension, a fusing together of the eye and heart, and then laid down (captured) onto the blank page by the hand. Intuitive apprehension seized by the heart, then filtered through the brain. Eyewitnesses talk about how rapid and accurate he could draw or sketch a portrait for a drink; how he seemed to enter and see the inside of his sitter.

In other words, his paintings are the result of the heart, aided by the eye, beating inside the brain. The result is a form of sensuous reason on the canvas, especially his nudes. This is why he dismissed Cubism. Fragmentation, the transforming of figures into multiple perspectives, was a form of lifeless barbarism to him. Nor was he interested in landscapes, still life, or reproducing the effects of light as were the Impressionists. He liked to work, instead, with models or people who happen to be around him, and create recognizable figures that expressed something about their inner selves. The inside made visible. Colour and light made to speak. The chaos of his life never expressed in his paintings.

"To paint, I have to have a living model in front of me. Abstraction exhausts and kills. It's an impasse. Let's be on guard against falling into the subsoil of the unconscious."

He would have opposed Surrealism if he had lived to see its birth.

I leave Villa Mimbelli and wander down to the water's edge.

There is a handful of sunbathers spread out across a series of flat, black rocks, catching the remains of the afternoon light. They lie on towels, like mermaids with newly formed limbs and sunglasses, a basket of snacks nearby. I look out at the water. Sunlight shines in irregularly cut sheets on the water, small waves fold and collapse on each other, and further out on the water sit the black hollow shapes, outlines really, of container ships against a distant, blank horizon. I watch two fit, smart-looking naval commanders—white caps with gold leaf, navy-blue uniforms with gold buttons and gold trim on the sleeves, white gloves—each with a small, black attaché case tucked under an arm. They both walk with purpose towards the Naval Academy until one of them drops one of his white gloves, and their stride for a moment must pause. The sea breeze blows across the road. A woman walks by eating an ice-cream cone, behind her is another woman in a light wool shawl pushing a baby stroller. Quotidian purpose and leisure. Something Modigliani was just not interested in, but strove, instead, for the purposeful, dreamy, unbound heights of art. The magic of art.

Modigliani was interested in painting and knowing beyond the physical surface of a person, seeing beyond the appearances. Hence, his interest in horoscopes, hashish, the occult, spiritualism—all vehicles to alternative ways of seeing and knowing. Modigliani wanted to find and express the reality past the surface, beyond the here and now. This, too, explains his rejection of Cubism and its cool abstract calculations and its desire to disorient the viewer, to redefine how one sees the everyday world.

I leave the museum and go to look for Caffè Bardi. It is supposed to be at the corner of Via Cairoli and Piazza Cavour. It is here

Modigliani and many of the local artists used to meet before it closed in 1921. Both the street and the piazza are still there. The piazza is not your usually shape, round or square, but more the shape of a very large cereal box, and the Caffè Bardi is gone. Instead, some four- or five-storey, well-kept, cream limestone buildings with pistachio-coloured shutters are on both sides of the square, and a series of small shops sell ice cream, shoes, umbrellas and some restaurant tables extend into the square. On the other side of the piazza, offices. There is not much more to the surface of things here. In fact, the surface of the sidewalk and street is very clean.

I am catching an early train tomorrow morning, 5:40 a.m. to be exact, to meet the editor of *The Dreaming Machine*. She has published excerpts from my last three books. I am also supposed to give a lecture to a Canadian Studies class at the University of Bologna on the topic of Canadian Identity and Poetry. As usual, other than a few notes in a small, silver-coiled notebook, I have not written much, so I decide the best thing to do is to have an early supper, sleep, and work on the train to Bologna.

My plan soon unravels. The restaurant I choose does not open until 8:30.

I wander into a Partito Democratico clubhouse and watch soccer in a big, dark hall with a wall-sized screen, to kill some time. Everyone is worshipping the match.

Now and again there are a few fists thrust into the air followed by groans or guffaws, or a singular flash of anger, depending on the play on the pitch.

I note the room is full of men, all old enough to be my grandfather. No one talks, no one smokes or drinks; complete silence except for the odd shuffle to the washroom.

I soon leave. It is only seven. I wander around the neighbourhood, note the very few night stars, laundry hanging on balconies, the quiet, yellow light inside a solitary butcher shop where the butcher and his only customer enjoy the process of buying supper as if it were the most important event of the day.

On a whim, I follow a group of noisy Italians who have just piled out of their car and are walking up the street in the opposite direction from me. I guess they are going out for dinner, and they certainly look like they know where to find a good place to eat. It turns out I am not wrong. The pasta carbonara is the best I have tasted since I was in Nice thirty years ago. I pass along my compliments to the waitress. She replies, "Why not tell Chef yourself? I will introduce you."

In the middle of our exchange, shortly after I asked him where he learned to cook (Milan, he says) and what brought him back to Livorno (a woman whom he did not end up marrying), he asks me what I am doing in Livorno.

"Looking for traces of Modigliani," I reply. "Then, write a book about him."

"And, did you find his traces? A complicated man, Modigliani, tragic and full of adventure. The adventure of discovering—oh, I don't know—is learning what you can do. Learning to do any art well is a great risk, a hazard."

He points to the crushed garlic: "That includes cooking."

And that, is it not, what draws us towards his life and legend as much as if we are drawn towards his art. Our perceptions of the "hazard" of Modigliani's life, fed by the romantic notions of the cursed, mad genius who lives only for his art.

His life, unfolding like a train wreck in slow motion: poverty, drink and drugs, rivalry, rage, passion, showmanship, neglect, complicated and often messy relationships with women, masks to hide the secret of his slow death, "artful dodger" poses, and finally an ending worthy of an Ancient Greek tragedy.

The spectacle of the impure artist's reach for purity, reach for beauty, backward and forward dance for recognition or what's a heaven for. "Wormwood, wormwood," said Hamlet. I wonder if Modigliani often thought the same thing about the pursuit, the same doubts, the same madness. His desire for beauty, his charm, search, doubts, imperfection, chaos, indifference, the line and colour of his nude models, his art, are all part of the DNA of his spirit,(our spirit), its darkness and light, masked/unmasked. Yet, it all feels like a tip of the brush/tongue comprehension, an almost revelation.

Lunia Czechowska's Dreams

**I returned to Paris in September 1920.

I wrote a few letters to Zbo while I was away, often inquiring about Modigliani.

He often wrote back, saying Modigliani returned to Livorno.

Back in Paris, Zbo, Hanka, and friends told me Modigliani gave up painting because of poor health. They also stopped talking about him in my presence.

This struck me as bizarre. Where did he go?

A few nights after my return, I had the strangest dreams. I was sleeping in the dining room on rue Joseph Bara (Zbo and Hanka's place) and the very room Modigliani had painted what would later be recognized as some of his masterpieces. I tossed and turned, unable to fall asleep. I dosed off and dreamed at first about my poor dead husband. He returned to Poland to fight for the Red Army, was wounded and taken prisoner, and later died in captivity. I then heard voices: drunk Modigliani and Utrillo shouting up at the window from the street below, "Come downstairs, sweet Lunia. We miss you! The wine is fine. Come out for a drink."

At first, the voices were full of laughter, then they became angry. I awoke to silence and the pale yellow-and-blue gaslit streetlamp's reflection flickering on the window. I fell asleep again and Modigliani appeared, wearing his brown corduroy jacket and vest, white shirt and paint-stained pants and boots. He was wearing his customary red, knotted scarf and big black hat. I thought he looked so handsome, so dashing, even though the strain of fatherhood and work showed on his face. We were walking together in a park in the quiet of the early morning. Chestnut leaves covered the grass, so it must have been the fall. A fine mist was lifting off the ground as the sun rose higher in the sky. He pulled out of his coat pocket what appeared to be a magazine or newspaper, opened it, pointed to a page and said, "Look, Lunia. It says here I've died. Don't you think that is a bit much! I'm not dead. You can see for yourself." Then Jeanne Hébuterne appeared—thin, floating mist parting in front of her as she walked towards us on the gravel path. She was dressed as an Ancient Greek woman. I could see the pleats in her drapery, her hair tied back in a bun, her face expressionless and serious, determined to meet us. She gestured to us and said, "Come back, come back..." her right hand moving, beckoning. His muse.

"There's Jeanne. Let's call her," I said to Modigliani. He then shouted out to Jeanne "No, no, in a minute."

I was so happy to see Jeanne and I waved at her to join us. I wanted to ask her about the new baby.

I then woke up.

Profit/Prophet

The American tourists came for a piece of him that summer. Pilgrims in search of the holy, tragic artist. The legend already high drama. The last act: wife, eight months pregnant, jumps two days after his death out of the fifth floor of her parents' home to her death. Perfect.

Must have sold his last painting palette five times, each time increasing the price by one hundred francs. Made sure orange bled into the yellow, and called it the last batch he used to paint nudes. Crushed a lipstick-stained Gauloise in the corner: his last lover's smoke. Ha ha. Sold his silver zinc tub.

Some things were impossible to sell: grey and weak early morning light in the studio; dirt-stained windows; pungent unwashed smell; wine stains; dried blood-red gobs of spit struck on the wall near the bed.

Loved selling his big black hat over and over. Easy to replace. Fetched a handsome price all over Montparnasse for a few years. And finally, yes, his paintings.

Endnotes

Pages 26-29. The poems are based on letters found in William Fifield, *Modigliani, The Biography*.

Page 48. Roger Wild quote is from William Fifield, *Modigliani, The Biography*.

Page 61. 'The insatiable fiery mouth...' is from William Fifield, *Modigliani, The Biography*.

Page 69. 'What good is the practice of modeling...' is from Jeffery Meyer, *Modigliani, A Life*.

Page 70. Augustus John quote is from Meryle Secrest, *Modigliani, A Life*.

Page 83. The Italian lines in the poem are from the poem 'Da Giorno per Giorno' by Giuseppe Ungaretti, *The Penguin Book of Italian Verse*, (1957).

Page 96. Mareva Voroben's account of the shooting incident at Chez Rosalie is from William Fitfield, *Modigliani, The Biography*.

Pages 96-97. The transformation of Beatrice Hastings' dress. There are two slightly different accounts: Jeffery Meyer, *Modigliani, A Life*, & Meryle Secrest, *Modigliani, A Life*.

Page 115. The anecdote about Zborowski taking an interest in Modigliani's models is from William Fifield, *Modigliani, The Biography*.

Page 128. The quoted letters are from Jeffery Meyer, *Modigliani, A Life*.

Acknowledgements

I wrote about Modigliani chronologically (birth to death), incorporating details, facts, and my own observations and responses to his life and paintings from the following books:

Modigliani, The Biography (William Morrow and Company, 1967) by William Fitfield.

Modigliani: The Poetry of Seeing, (Taschen, 2017) by Doris Krystof.

Modigliani: A Life, (Harcourt, Inc., 2006) by Jeffery Meyers.

Modigliani, Man and Myth, (The Orion Press, 1958) by Jeanne Modigliani.

Modigliani and His Models, (Royal Academy of Arts, London, 2006) edited by Simonetta Fraquelli & Norman Rosenthal.

Modigliani: A Life, (Alfred A. Knope, 2011) by Meryle Secrest.

Although Max Jacob kept a journal, the one represented here is entirely fictional but based on various documented events. As a poet, painter, writer, critic, and general flaneur in Montparnasse at the turn of the century, he was friends with many of the shining lights in the quartier. The list includes Guillaume Apollinaire, Jean Cocteau, Beatrice Hastings, Jean Hugo, Moïse Kisling, Amedeo Modigliani, Jean Pascin, Pablo Picasso, Chaïm Soutine, Maurice Utrillo and André Utter.

I used, as well, the names of real people, dates, and their recorded personal situations and opinions found in the books above. In some cases, I imagined characters speaking, expanded on or condensed historical situations, enriched or collapsed phrases and observations, and generally behaved like an alchemist all in service towards representing a larger truth found in fiction and poetry.

Modigliani's horoscope is a modified version of a more detailed chart created on my request by Gino Mazzei, artist, M.A. MFA. Thanks Gino.

The poems "October 1909, Brâncuşi Studio," "Anna Akhmatova," and "Multiples of Me" were originally published in *The Dreaming Machine No. 4*, online world literature journal, May 1, 2019, edited by Pina Piccolo, Bologna, Italy.

A suite of nine Modigliani poems and one fictional Max Jacob journal entry were originally published in *The Stone Mason's Notebook*, Ekstasis Editions, 2016.

My thanks to Michael Carrino for taking the time to read the manuscript as I worked on it.

Carmelo Militano is the author of two books of poetry (*Morning After You* and *The Stone Mason's Notebook*) as well as three books of prose (*The Fate of Olives, Sebastiano's Vine* and *Lost Aria*). He is the winner of the F.G. Bressani award for poetry and each of his prose works have been short-listed for various literary awards. *Catching Desire* is his sixth book.